NURSING AT BART'S

St Bartholomew's Hospital, 1720.

NURSING AT BART'S

A History of Nursing Service and
Nurse Education at St Bartholomew's Hospital,
London

Geoffrey Yeo

First published in the United Kingdom in 1995
by St Bartholomew and Princess Alexandra and Newham College of
Nursing and Midwifery

ISBN 0 9526520 0 5 (case)
ISBN 0 9526520 1 3 (paperback)

Produced by Alan Sutton Publishing Ltd.,
Stroud, Glos.
Printed in Great Britain by
Alden Press, Oxford and Northampton.

CONTENTS

INTRODUCTION

Ye shall also faithfully and charitably serve, and helpe the poore in al their grieves and diseases, as well by kepyng them swete and cleane, as in gevyng theim their meates and drinkes after the moste honest and comfortable maner.

Charge to Sisters,
from 'The Ordre of the Hospital of St Bartholomewes in Westsmythfielde', 1552.

You shall faithfully and humanely serve and help the patients in all their griefs and diseases, as well in keeping them sweet and clean in their persons, bedding and in every other respect, as in giving them their meat and drink after the most honest and comfortable manner.

Charge to Sisters, *c.*1930.

For almost 900 years St Bartholomew's Hospital has occupied its original site in Smithfield, in the City of London, where it was founded in March 1123. It has a long tradition of nursing care and has played a leading role in the education of nurses for over a century. Since Victorian times nurses have formed by far the largest group of staff in the Hospital. In many historical studies, however, their work has received scant attention. Sir Norman Moore's monumental *History of St Bartholomew's Hospital*, published in 1918, devotes more than 300 pages to medicine and surgery but only 23 to nursing. An attempt to redress the balance now seems due. This book provides an account of the origins of nursing at Bart's and the growth of educational provision for nurses. It also describes the development of the Hospital's nursing service to patients, and changing attitudes to nurses and their work.

St Bartholomew's has a particular significance to students of the history of nursing, for no other hospital in the United Kingdom has had a continuous history of patient care since the early years of the twelfth century. In the medieval period it was just one of many English hospitals where the sick might be received, but at the Reformation all the rest were closed or converted to other uses. After a period of great uncertainty, St Bartholomew's alone survived as a general hospital, receiving a new constitution by royal charter in the winter of 1546–7. St Thomas' Hospital in Southwark was closed for several years but re-opened in 1551–2. For a century and a half these were the only two general hospitals in England, and their nursing structures naturally formed a model for the new hospital foundations of the eighteenth and nineteenth centuries. The formal education of nurses began in the 1860s in the Nightingale School at St Thomas' Hospital, while the subsequent bitterly-fought campaign for registration and professional standards took much of its inspiration from the work of Mrs Bedford Fenwick and her successor Isla Stewart at St Bartholomew's.

The larger part of this book is concerned with the period after the establishment of the School of Nursing at Bart's in 1877, which saw more rapid and far-reaching changes than any previous era. In many ways the history of these changes is typical of developments throughout the United Kingdom. Nevertheless, as the Sisters' charges indicate, some traditions proved remarkably resistant to change, and in a number of respects Bart's long remained distinctive. However in recent years, while St Bartholomew's has maintained its reputation as a centre of excellence, most of its nursing practices have been assimilated to the norms of the National Health Service, and much that I have written in the last chapters of this book would be equally true of many other hospitals in London and elsewhere.

Much of the research for the book was undertaken in 1992–3, when I was head of the Archives Department at St Bartholomew's Hospital. When I began this study, few who worked at Bart's could have foreseen that the Hospital was about to enter a new period of crisis, unparalleled since the sixteenth century, and that for the second time in its history it was to face the possibility of closure. Despite public outcry, both the government and the Regional Health Authority appeared determined that the Smithfield site should be vacated, and plans were announced for St Bartholomew's and the Royal London Hospital to be merged on a single site at Whitechapel. Writing objectively at a time of high emotion has not been easy, especially when the patients' 'Save Bart's Campaign' had set up its headquarters outside my office door. Now that the book is finished, I hope it will prove acceptable to historians of nursing and nurse education as well as those who know the Hospital. It was begun at the suggestion of Susan Studdy, then Principal of the St Bartholomew's College of Nursing and Midwifery, but I have been allowed full editorial freedom and responsibility for what I have written is mine alone.

I am grateful to all who have offered assistance in my research. Many nurses kindly supplied information or agreed to be interviewed: Sybil Allen, formerly Head of Nursing Services (Orthopaedic and Accident and Emergency); Carol Bavin, Lecturer, St Bartholomew and Princess Alexandra and Newham College of Nursing and Midwifery; Margaret Cartwright, formerly Vice-Principal of the College; Elsie Hall, formerly Sister Harmsworth; Pat Haworth, formerly Sister Bowlby; Pamela Hibbs, Chief Nurse and Director of Quality Assurance, The Royal Hospitals NHS Trust; and Mary Walker, formerly Sister Waring. Evelyn Swabey provided reminiscences of her time as a probationer in the 1930s, and Winifred Hector, Principal Tutor 1946–70, allowed me to see the typescript of her unpublished autobiography. The staff of the Department of Medical Photography, St Bartholomew's Hospital Medical College, assisted in supplying some of the illustrations. Susan McGann, Archivist of the Royal College of Nursing, provided valuable background material. No book of this kind could be written without access to archival sources, and acknowledgement is also due to those who have worked to ensure the preservation of the Hospital's archives: my predecessors Gweneth Whitteridge, Veronica Stokes, Nellie Kerling and Janet Foster, my former colleague Judith Etherton, and the present archivists, Andrew Griffin and Caroline Jones, whose support and encouragement have allowed me to bring the book to completion.

Geoffrey Yeo
April 1995

Chapter One

THE MEDIEVAL HOSPITAL: 1123–1546

The professional skills of the modern nurse were unknown when St Bartholomew's Hospital was founded by Rahere in the year 1123. Medical care and nursing as we recognise them today did not exist in London in the twelfth century. Hospitals at that time were religious foundations whose principal object was to provide a comfortable environment for the sick poor in the hope that rest, regular meals and constant prayer would supply them with a cure. Over 400 years were to pass after the founding of Bart's before the first physicians and surgeons were appointed; five centuries intervened before there were any members of staff with the title of 'nurse'; and more than 750 years stand between Rahere and the time when nursing was first recognised as a profession and the duties and responsibilities of nurses began to take their present shape.

A 'nurse' in medieval England was not an attendant on the sick, but a woman who took charge of young children and cared for them in place of an absent mother. Among the most notable of these women was Joan (or Joanna) Astley, who nursed the infant King Henry VI in 1424. In later life she lived in West Smithfield, within the precinct of St Bartholomew's Hospital.[1] A tablet on the wall of the former Pathological Block in Smithfield marks the approximate site of her house.[2] However Joan Astley was a tenant of St Bartholomew's rather than a member of staff, and while she must have been familiar with the Hospital she is not known to have tended patients there. Those who regularly undertook this task at St Bartholomew's in the middle ages were not nurses, but members of the Augustinian order who had entered the religious life to serve God by caring for the sick.

In the earliest centuries of the Hospital's existence its head was known as the Master and his staff were the Brothers and Sisters of the Hospital. In 1316 an order was made that there should be seven Brothers and four Sisters, who were to receive their monastic habits after taking vows and swearing obedience in the priory church of St Bartholomew the Great.[3] Brothers and Sisters alike were expected to be regular in attendance at divine worship and to hear mass every morning, although only Brothers were entitled to attend the Chapter at which administrative business was

1

The medieval Hospital: an artist's impression (by Ernest Coffin, c.1923).

conducted. A fourteenth-century Bishop of London gave instructions that both the Brothers and the Sisters should be 'diligent and pious in serving the sick' and should obey the Master's orders regarding care of the infirm, ensuring that none were sent away unrecovered. By the sixteenth century, however, the day-to-day care of the sick poor had devolved on the Sisters. In 1535 the King's commissioners reported that the Sisters were responsible for giving patients their food and other necessities, and in the mid 1540s it was stated that the particular task of the four Sisters was to 'minister to the poor'. There is practically no documentary evidence of their daily work, but their duties may have included baking, brewing, spinning and weaving, besides feeding the patients and making them comfortable. All we know for certain about the life of the medieval Sisters is that they wore grey tunics and that each received a daily allowance of bread and half a flagon of beer.[4]

One of the first recorded Sisters was a woman named Isabel, daughter of Edward de Bray, who lived in the mid thirteenth century. She owned a house near St Paul's Cathedral, which she gave to the Hospital so that she could join its community as a Sister and devote her life to the performance of her duty towards the sick.[5] Some fifty years earlier there is a mention of Edeva, daughter of Wakerilda of Writtle in Essex, who was a servant of William Bocuinte, Sheriff of London in 1193. William wished to make provision for Edeva by giving her ten shillings yearly for life. This sum was to consist of seven shillings from rent of land in Smithfield and three shillings

2

from other sources. William further indicated that if Edeva should decide to enter St Bartholomew's Hospital and take the habit of a Sister, then at her death the annual payment of ten shillings would be given to the Hospital. Since William's sealed deed was preserved at St Bartholomew's it seems likely that Edeva chose to join the Hospital and is therefore the first Sister whose name is known.[6]

Other records mention Sister Joan, granddaughter of Adam de Wytheby, who in 1250 or 1251 gave the Hospital the right to collect certain rents in a street near the River Thames;[7] and Sister Emma Charbury, who in the fifteenth century was apparently responsible for rebuilding three shops within the Hospital precincts.[8] In 1348 William de Pertenhale made his will leaving property near Wood Street, in the City of London, to be given to St Bartholomew's after the death of his daughter Joan who was a Sister in the Hospital.[9] In each case, however, information about these early Sisters is very limited: they appear as little more than shadowy figures from the distant

A thirteenth-century deed in the Hospital archives. One of two surviving documents concerning a gift to the Hospital from Sister Joan, granddaughter of Adam de Wytheby.

3

past. Women such as Joan de Pertenhale and Isabel de Bray probably came from wealthier families than the majority, and their names are known because of the property transactions in which they were involved. Most of those who cared for patients at St Bartholomew's brought no property to the Hospital, and even their names are not recorded. Although we can see in their work something of the antecedents of modern nursing, their chief legacy has been the title of 'Sister', which has never gone out of use at Bart's and has been adopted by other hospitals throughout the British Isles.

Chapter Two

FROM ROSE FISHER TO BETSEY PRIG:
1546–1869

In the 1540s the old order was swept away when the monastic life was abolished at the Reformation. Almost all of London's medieval hospitals disappeared. St Bartholomew's was threatened with extinction but ultimately survived the upheavals of religious change, emerging as a largely secular foundation. The Master and Brothers were replaced by a President, Treasurer and Board of Governors, whose members were chosen from the civic dignitaries of the City. In the winter months of 1546–7 the new constitution of the Hospital was laid down by royal charter of King Henry VIII. Medical staff were to be appointed, and the accommodation, which six months earlier had comprised only 45 beds, was to be much enlarged. There were to be lodgings sufficient for one hundred poor patients, and 'one Matron and twelve women under her to make the beds and wash and attend upon the said poor'.[1]

The post of Matron was not wholly new. The staffing structure was probably copied from that of the Savoy Hospital, founded by the King a little over twenty years earlier, where there had been 'one Matron with twelve other women . . . not married, of the age of 36 years or more'.[2] At St Bartholomew's a Matron is first mentioned in the autumn of 1546, a few months before King Henry's charter. The role envisaged for her can be reconstructed from a book of orders drawn up in 1552 under the authority of the City Corporation. These included a 'charge', or set of instructions, for each of the officers of the Hospital. The Matron was told to receive patients on their admission and to place them in the wards, to supervise her assistants, and to take responsibility for all the beds, sheets, coverlets and blankets.[3] The first known Matron of St Bartholomew's was Rose Fisher. No record of her appointment survives, but her name appears in the Hospital's archives from 1547 to 1559.[4]

The royal charter made no mention of Sisters; the Matron's assistants were to be simply 'twelve women'. However in August 1550 the Board of Governors decreed that 'the Sisters of the house' should fetch the patients' food, and in the orders of 1552 detailed instructions were given for the conduct of Sisters. It is clear that the old name remained in use by common consent. In 1552 the Sisters were told that they should be gentle and

Of the Hospitall.
The Sisters.

YOur charge is, in al thin-ges to declare and shewe your selues gentle diligēt and obedient to the Matrone of this house who is appointed & aucthorised to be your chief go-uerneresse and ruler.

Ye shall also faithfully and charitably serue, and helpe the poore in al their grieues and di-seases, aswell by kepyng them swete and cleane, as in geuyng them their meates and drinkes after the moste honest & cōforta ble maner. Also ye shall vse vn-to them good and honest talke, suche as may comforte & amend them, and vtterly to aduoyde all lyght, wanton, and foolishe wordes, gestures and maners, vsyng youre selues vnto them with all sobrietie and discretion. And aboue all thynges se that ye auoyde, abhorre and detest skoldyng, and dronkennesse, as moste pestilēt and filthie vices.

Instructions to the Sisters, from the book of orders drawn up for the Hospital in 1552. 'Your charge is in all things to declare and show yourselves gentle, diligent and obedient to the Matron of this house . . .'.

diligent, obedient to the Matron, and faithful and charitable in serving the poor. More specifically they were expected to keep the patients clean, give them their meat and drink, make their beds and wash their clothes, and 'use unto them good and honest talk, such as may comfort and amend them'. They were to avoid 'light, wanton and foolish words', scolding, drunkenness and male company. When they were not occupied with the patients, the Matron was to set them spinning flax or give them other suitable work to keep them from idleness. At night they were to stay in their own quarters unless they had the Matron's permission to attend a patient.[5]

There is no evidence of any dispute over the continuance of the name Sister with its overtones of the old religious basis of the Hospital. The Sisters of the reformed Hospital had no religious duties, but the perpetuation of the old name suggests that their work of cleaning, feeding and comforting the patients was seen as little different from that of their predecessors. Certainly the tradition of chastity was maintained, for in 1560 a Sister who wanted to marry was dismissed. Practical considerations might have been at issue, a husband being seen as an impediment to her work; but the reason given for her dismissal was simply that a married Sister was contrary to 'the old custom'. When St Thomas' Hospital was refounded in Southwark in 1551–2 the same rule was enforced there.[6]

One of the first decisions made at St Bartholomew's by the newly established Board of Governors was to place an order for russet cloth for the Matron's 'livery' or uniform. The Sisters initially also wore russet, but in 1554 the Governors purchased lengths of watchett, a blue cloth, for the Sisters' liveries. Blue was still worn by Bart's Sisters in the last decade of the twentieth century, and it is believed that blue uniforms have been used continuously in the Hospital since the 1550s.[7]

It seems likely that the long-established system, whereby each Sister was responsible for a single ward, also dates from this period. When St Bartholomew's was founded there may have been only one ward to house all the patients in the Hospital, but by the sixteenth century the sexes had been segregated into separate wards. In the orders of 1552 it was laid down that without the Matron's approval no Sister should visit a patient at night, 'not though it be in her ward'. This is the first indication in the surviving records that each ward had been assigned to a particular Sister. It appears from inventories preserved in the Hospital archives that by the 1590s there were about twelve or thirteen wards, each supervised by a Ward Sister.[8]

Much of the Sisters' time was occupied in spinning, a task which was essential to ensure an adequate supply of linen for the needs of the Hospital. The Governors provided the flax and the Matron issued it to the Sisters; when spun it was returned by her to the Governors who then arranged for it to be weighed and woven.[9] Spinning is mentioned less frequently in the seventeenth century. By the 1650s it was viewed as an occupation for the female patients rather than the Sisters, though as late as 1678 the Governors were instructing the Matron to buy hemp to be spun to make cloth for the Hospital.[10]

With no other staff attached to the wards, the Sisters were expected to undertake virtually all the day-to-day work, much of it at a menial level. The floors of the wards were strewn with rushes, and the patients lay on straw mattresses; both had to be taken to the Sisters' garden for burning when they were soiled. Even before the arrival of a pumped water supply in 1676 the Hospital employed a labourer to carry buckets of water to the wards, but the transport of coal and of food and drink from the kitchen was left to the Sisters.[11] They also emptied the slops, did the cleaning and even whitewashed the wards.[12] They had to wash all the patients' personal and bed linen, by pounding it in a large wooden vat known as the Buck. This task, performed at three-weekly intervals, was called 'beating' the Buck. It was very strenuous, and the Sisters undertook the job in rotation. They supplied their own wood-ash (soap was not used until 1687), and every sheet had to be accounted for to the Matron. Each Sister was responsible for the sheets used in her own ward and for drying, pressing and mending them.[13]

From the mid seventeenth century, however, they were offered more assistance. By 1648 the older Sisters were excused the heavy work of beating the Buck, and later a 'buck woman' was engaged to assist them, though the Sisters remained responsible for washing the linen until 1754.[14] In 1661 the Governors conceded that if a Sister was too old, or too sick, to fetch bread and beer in person, then an 'honest patient' could be asked to assist her.[15] In the previous year the Hospital had recruited two men to carry coal,[16] and other helpers had been employed in the wards from the 1640s onwards. These changes were brought about by an influx of additional patients, wounded soldiers and sailors from the English Civil War and the Anglo-Dutch naval wars. Helpers for the Sisters are first mentioned in 1647, and in 1650 there were four such assistants in the Hospital. In February 1652 the Governors agreed that Margaret Whitaker, who had been a helper and a nurse for five years past, should have the next Sister's post to fall vacant. At the same time they adopted a rule that only those who had been a nurse and had worked at the Buck should be eligible for appointment as a Sister. The Hospital accounts record a payment to a nurse on 13 April 1650. These are the first occasions when the word 'nurse' is used in the records of St Bartholomew's Hospital.[17] After 1652 more helpers and nurses were employed. Their chief tasks appear to have been cleaning the wards and

A wounded soldier: this wooden statue in the Great
Hall at Bart's dates from the seventeenth century when
many injured soldiers and sailors were cared for in the
Hospital.

assisting at the Buck. At first the terms 'nurse' and 'helper' were used interchangeably, but by the 1670s it was broadly established that the status of helper was inferior to that of a nurse, just as the nurses were themselves subordinate to the Sisters.[18]

Each Sister was expected to take charge of the medicines prescribed for the patients in her ward. In 1633, when William Harvey was Physician to the Hospital, the Board of Governors agreed to Harvey's suggestion that the Matron and Sisters should be required to attend the Physician 'when he sitteth to give directions and prescriptions, that they may fully conceive his directions and what is to be done'. They were also instructed to report any patients who would not present themselves for examination or refused to

9

take their medicine.[19] Early in the next century the Governors found it necessary to remind the nurses that each patient's prescription had to be kept separately, and to warn them against putting several medicines in the same bottle or pot.[20]

Following the Governors' ruling of 1652, no Sister should have been employed who did not have previous experience as a nurse or helper. Although the rule was not always observed, many nurses subsequently won promotion to the rank of Sister. On the other hand the Matrons of the seventeenth century were always recruited from outside the Hospital; it was evidently not felt appropriate for Sisters to be promoted to this post. Matrons were generally wives or widows of tradesmen, with previous experience in matters of household management. Margaret Blague, Matron from 1643 to 1675, was the widow of a barber-surgeon and sister-in-law of the Clerk to the Governors. During the Great Plague of 1665, when the medical staff fled to the country, she conscientiously remained at her post and helped to keep the Hospital open to patients, disregarding the risk to her own safety.[21]

The status of women like Margaret Blague was reflected in the salary which they received. In 1550 the Matron had been paid a yearly salary of a little over three pounds, plus one shilling and four pence per week for her 'board wages'. The Sisters' salary at that time was two pounds, plus one shilling and three pence per week. In effect the Matron had been the senior Sister, taking charge of her colleagues but expected to join with them in spinning flax.[22] A century later the differential was much greater. In the 1660s Sisters received two pounds and ten shillings yearly, and three shillings and six pence per week for board wages, a rate of pay which contrasted unfavourably with the forty pounds paid annually to the Matron.[23] In addition the Matron had the right to the 'profits of her cellar', a monopoly on the sale of beer within the Hospital precincts. Despite repeated attempts by the Governors to abolish this privilege, it survived until 1706 and was a source of considerable further income.[24]

While the Hospital required its Matron to be a woman of some ability and social standing, these qualities were evidently not expected of the Sisters and nurses, who were recruited on the basis of their physical strength and their willingness to undertake the constant heavy work of washing and cleaning. In the circumstances it is not surprising to find that they sometimes proved unsatisfactory. In July 1647 the Board of Governors heard complaints that the Sister in Diet Ward was slack in her morning duties and used abusive language to the patients in her charge. She was reprimanded and threatened with dismissal if the offences were repeated. In the years which followed growing numbers of complaints about Sisters were brought before the

Governors. Between 1655 and 1700 no fewer than twentyone were dismissed for misbehaviour, an average of about one dismissal every two years at a time when there were fifteen Sister's posts in the Hospital. The average number of reprimands over the same period was about one per year.[25] It is not clear whether the increase in disciplinary proceedings was due to a growing severity on the part of the Governors, the employment of a lower class of women, or increased pressure on the nursing staff following the influx of soldiers and sailors into the Hospital. The commonest offences were negligence, extortion and theft, whether of the Hospital's sheets and blankets or of the patients' personal belongings. Other misdemeanours included drunkenness, disorderly behaviour and keeping company with men.[26] One Sister was disciplined for selling 'pots of physic' to strangers, another for eavesdropping outside the room where the Governors held their meetings. Sister Jane Rawlins was dismissed 'for selling physic to the patients and advising them to take things contrary to the doctor's order'. The Sisters had also become negligent about wearing their uniforms, and in 1685 were instructed to 'buy themselves liveries of blue cloth . . . as anciently hath been accustomed'.[27] On several occasions the Governors felt it necessary to remind the Sisters and nurses that they were forbidden to demand money from patients or to drink with them or induce them to go to public houses.[28] The constant reminders make it clear that these practices remained widespread. Their offences reflect something of the restricted lives which the Sisters led: a routine of drudgery and manual labour, from which drink offered an easy if temporary escape.

Some of the early Matrons of St Bartholomew's Hospital were married women, but the rule that Sisters should be single women or widows was strictly enforced. A Sister who married faced immediate dismissal.[29] Even widows sometimes caused difficulties by trying to bring their children to live with them in the Hospital, and for this reason the Governors preferred to appoint women with no family encumbrances. As a result many of the staff had no-one to look after them in old age, and continued working until infirmity finally compelled them to give up.[30] In 1721 Lettice Dynn, Sister in Curtain Ward, was still working at the age of eighty, but was then retired on a pension from the Governors because her incapacity had led her to set fire to the bed curtains. She had worked at St Bartholomew's for more than thirty years and had never once been reprimanded.[31] Indeed all the reprimands and dismissals recorded in the late 1600s and early 1700s were for disciplinary offences; no Sister was dismissed simply for incompetence. Since the Governors allowed Lettice Dynn to become dangerously incapacitated before offering her a pension, they were evidently prepared to tolerate very low levels of ability on the part of the nursing staff.

All the Sisters and nurses lived in the Hospital and were forbidden to spend the night outside the precincts without permission.[32] As early as the 1550s the Matron had an apartment of her own,[33] but the Sisters slept together in a ward set aside for their use. This accommodation was known at first as the 'women's ward' and later as the 'Sisters' room' or 'Sisters' chamber'.[34] The communal sleeping quarters remained in use until the mid eighteenth century when the Governors decided that all the old buildings should be demolished and the Hospital reconstructed. Four blocks around an open Square were erected to the design of James Gibbs between 1730 and 1768. Three of these – the South, West and East Wings – contained the wards, while the North Wing was the administrative block. In the new buildings each Sister was given her own accommodation in a separate room where she could sleep next to her ward.[35]

The number of Sisters, set at twelve in the charter of Henry VIII, had increased to fifteen by the mid seventeenth century, and to twenty by the 1730s. By 1773 there were thirty Sisters in the Hospital. The complement of four helpers or nurses in 1650 had grown to fifteen by 1773, but there was still only one nurse to every two Sisters. Not until 1782 was the number of nurses increased to thirty, so that for the first time there were equal

The Square of St Bartholomew's Hospital in 1752. The North Wing is on the right, the newly built West Wing on the left.

A detail from William Hogarth's painting The Pool of Bethesda *on the Grand Staircase in the North Wing. These figures are thought to be modelled on patients at Bart's in the eighteenth century.*

numbers of Sisters and nurses.[36] It is assumed that each ward could then be staffed during daylight hours by one Sister and one nurse.

Night staff were also employed. In the seventeenth century the wards had been unattended at night, but in 1745 the records first mention 'watchers', living outside the Hospital, who undertook duty in the wards from dusk until dawn.[37] In 1771 the Matron, Susannah Robinson, reported to the Governors that she supervised 'upwards of one hundred' staff, including helpers and watchers as well as Sisters and nurses. She added that since

13

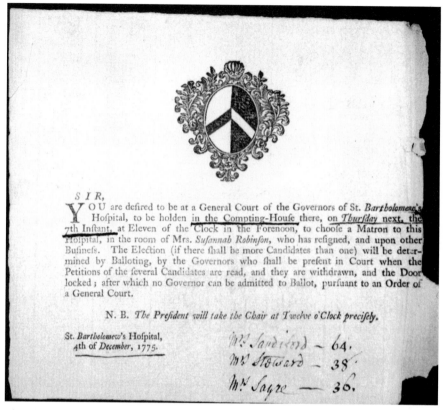

A notice summoning Governors to elect a new Matron, following the resignation of Susannah Robinson in 1775. A majority of votes was cast for Martha Sandiford, who held office from 1775 to 1781.

'the happiness and quiet of the patients greatly depends upon the qualification and disposition of the persons employed to attend them', much of her time was occupied in 'enquiring after their characters, interposing in . . . disputes and squabbles between the Sisters, nurses, helpers and patients, and removing the Sisters and nurses into different wards as their capacities best suit'.[38]

Her statement also indicates the other tasks performed by the Matron. She had the custody and care of the Hospital's linen, whether used by the patients, the Surgeons, or at the Governors' table; she kept an account of all money due to the Sisters and nurses; she checked everything that was sent to, and returned by, the washerwoman; and she bought each year 5000 yards of tape for surgical use, 4000 yards of Russia cloth for making into towels, 5000 yards of Irish cloth for making sheets, as well as flock for bolsters and pillows and much else besides. She also bought material for shirts, shifts, caps, handkerchiefs, aprons and petticoats which were given to the poor patients. For these duties she received a yearly salary of £40, with a gratuity of £20. She asked the Governors for an increase in salary and was granted £80 per annum, with the same gratuity as before.[38]

Further details of the Matron's work are given in a set of instructions approved by the Board of Governors in 1803. In that year Mary Foote was elected Matron and was told that she would be expected to receive all female patients on admission and allocate them to convenient places in the wards. She was also to attend the discharge of patients, which at that time took place once a week on Thursday morning. She was to make a daily inspection of the wards, the laundry and the kitchen, ensuring that the Sisters and nurses performed their duty in making beds and keeping the wards clean. The nursing staff were to give her an account of the clothes and money of patients who could not take care of their own possessions, and when the Sisters and nurses were not otherwise occupied she was to set them to work mending sheets and bedding for the Hospital.[39]

The earliest surviving illustrations of wards at St Bartholomew's date from the first half of the nineteenth century.[40] In the 1820s there were 26 wards, all within the Gibbs buildings which faced onto the Square. Their sizes varied, for in some cases large 'double' wards had been created by demolishing part of the wall that originally separated each pair of adjoining wards. Some still had old wooden bedsteads, but in others iron beds had been brought into use in 1815. They were furnished with curtains, flock mattresses and bolsters, as well as sheets and blankets. Each ward had an open fire for warmth, and candles were used for lighting until the introduction of gas in the 1840s. There were tables and benches in the wards, but in general the furnishing was very sparse. The walls were painted a dull drab colour, and the use of decorations and flowers was unknown until the latter part of the century. Water was pumped to each floor of the building, and after 1812 slipper baths were regularly provided in the wards, although patients who needed a full bath had to be taken to the basement which contained the bath-house.[41]

The early nineteenth century is also the first period when the role of the nurses can be clearly distinguished from that of the Sisters who supervised them. The nurses were expected to put sheets on the beds, wash the pans and plates used at meals and clean the floors, bedsteads and other furniture. They also collected bread, milk and provisions for the ward. For these tasks they were theoretically allowed to seek help from convalescent patients, but in practice this source of assistance was little used and in their other duties the nurses worked unaided. They examined patients on admission to see whether they were free from vermin and provided with suitable clothing.

Rahere Ward, West Wing, in the 1830s.

They helped the patients in and out of bed, warmed their drinks and cleaned the bedding of those who were incontinent. Dressings were the responsibility of doctors rather than nurses, but rules drawn up in 1814 stated that the nurses were to assist the medical staff 'during the whole time of dressing the patients' and were also to administer fomentations, enemas and emetics. At surgical operations they were to 'attend and assist the patients', presumably by offering them comfort and support during their ordeal, since anaesthesia was still unknown. When a patient died, it was the nurse's duty to strip and lay out the body and to give notice to the beadles for removal to the mortuary.[42]

In the nineteenth century the 'watchers' and 'helpers' were heard of no more. In 1814 the Hospital was still employing 'night nurses' but most of the day nurses were also expected to undertake night duty in rotation. Nurses working at night were to place a clean chamber-pot at each bed, to take orders from their Sister as to what nourishment the patients might need and to visit 'every weak patient's bedside' at least hourly. They were also instructed to keep a light and a fire burning in the ward and to be ready at a moment's notice to attend on patients who called for help. They were warned that if they fell asleep while on duty they were liable to be dismissed.[42]

Following the custom of the Hospital, Sisters were generally known by the names of their wards rather than their surnames. Some of the wards were named to commemorate the virtues, and thus St Bartholomew's had a Sister Faith, a Sister Hope and a Sister Charity; Sister Radcliffe and Sister Kenton worked in wards named after eminent benefactors; and the use of biblical names meant that there was a Sister Luke as well as a Sister Martha.[43] Other members of staff sometimes worked with Sisters for many years without knowing their true names. The habit of suppressing a Sister's personal name may have encouraged the idea that she devoted the whole of her life to serving the patients in her ward, and perhaps for this reason the practice was adopted in a number of other hospitals.

A Sister still had some routine tasks which were not delegated to the nurses: she received coal deliveries for the ward, and carried medicines from the Apothecary's shop and linen to and from the laundry. However most of her duties were at a more responsible level. Every Friday morning she read aloud in her ward the Governors' rules for the conduct of the patients, and much of her time was devoted to ensuring that the rules were obeyed. It was she who saw that patients did not leave the ward until discharged, and who enforced the edicts against allowing their friends to stay in the ward, against permitting articles for sale and against smoking or playing cards and dice. It was her responsibility to accompany patients who were to be discharged; to inform the Matron and the Apothecary of the death of a patient; and, if she was Sister of a ground floor ward, to take her turn in locking the iron gate at the entrance to the building.[42]

By the 1830s a Sister was expected to be of sufficient calibre to 'carry into effect the directions of the medical officers' regarding the patients' welfare. In particular, she received instructions from the medical staff about the patients' diet, which she daily reported to the Hospital cook. The reception of provisions from the cook, and their correct distribution to the patients, was also her responsibility. She was expected to report to the medical staff any changes which she might observe in the patients' symptoms, and to take charge of and administer the medicines which had been prescribed for patients in her ward. Only in the Sister's absence was this duty to be undertaken by a nurse.[42]

Sisters and nurses alike were required to be regular in attendance at services in the Hospital's parish church of St Bartholomew the Less. In the late seventeenth century the Hospital would admit only members of the Church of England to posts on the nursing staff, and in 1699 a Sister who was found to be a Roman Catholic was dismissed. The rule regarding church attendance had been imposed in 1652 and was reiterated in 1756 with the further stipulation that the Sisters should walk to church in procession. A special white cloak called a 'night rail' was worn by the Sisters on these occasions. In the early nineteenth century the Matron and Sisters were expected to attend morning service every Sunday, and the nurses attended in the evening. They assembled in the North Wing, dressed in full uniform, and proceeded from there to the church, taking with them all the patients from their wards who were fit enough to attend.[44]

Despite this enforced religious observance, the traditional picture of nursing at this period is of ignorant, drunken and slovenly women, typified by Sarah Gamp, the nurse in Charles Dickens's novel *Martin Chuzzlewit*. According to Dickens, Mrs Gamp was 'a fat old woman . . . in dilapidated articles of dress'; her face 'was somewhat red and swollen, and it was difficult to enjoy her society without becoming conscious of a smell of spirits'. Sarah Gamp is represented as a self-employed 'monthly nurse' or midwife, but her equally disreputable partner Betsey Prig is described as 'recommended from Bartholomew's' and as 'a fair specimen of a Hospital nurse'.[45]

Dickens was writing in the 1840s. His picture was probably more true of self-employed than of Hospital nurses; within the Hospital it was perhaps a more apt description of the nurses than of the Sisters. In the mid nineteenth century nurses at St Bartholomew's were generally middle-aged women of what was then called 'the domestic-servant class'. Some were widows, and many were said to have taken up nursing when other occupations failed. When the Charity Commissioners inspected the Hospital in 1836–7 they reported that the nurses performed 'all the usual duties of servants'. Fifty years later the distinguished surgeon Sir James Paget wrote his recollections of the nurses who worked at Bart's when he was a medical student in the 1830s. 'The greater part of them', he recalled, 'were rough, dull, unobservant and untaught'. Even of the best nurses of those days 'it could only be said that they were kindly, and careful and attentive in doing what they were told'. Of the Sisters, on the other hand, the Charity Commissioners reported that they 'have usually been persons who have received some education and have lived in a respectable rank of life'. James Paget gave the Sisters of the 1830s a further testimonial. Some, he wrote, were excellent, 'especially . . . in the medical wards, where everything was more gentle and more orderly than in the surgical. There was an admirable Sister Hope, who had had her leg amputated in the Hospital and then spent her life in giving others the most kindly watchful care. Sister Mary, a near relative of hers, was as constant to her charge. They had none of the modern art; they could not have kept a chart or skilfully taken a temperature, but they had an admirable sagacity and a sort of rough practical knowledge which were nearly as good as any acquired skill'.[46]

A nurse in Rahere Ward, 1844.

A fondness for drink was certainly not unknown, among Sisters and nurses alike. In 1775 Hester Hill was dismissed for selling gin to the patients, and in 1782 another Sister, Ann Dubarcow, was discharged from office 'for drunkenness and other misbehaviour'.[47] An amusing story is told of John Abernethy, Surgeon to the Hospital in the early nineteenth century, leaning on his walking-stick while talking to his colleagues in the Square. As a nurse walked past them, Abernethy swung his stick and brought it into contact with a bulge under her dress, exclaiming 'If that is not a bottle of gin, ma'm, I beg your pardon'. His diagnosis was correct, and the bottle lay shattered in pieces on the ground.[48]

Between 1786 and 1800 four Sisters and two nurses were dismissed for drunkenness, two Sisters and one nurse for theft, and four Sisters and one nurse for other offences, including disorderly behaviour and pawning the Hospital's sheets.[49] When the duties of the Hospital Steward were set out in 1833 he was required to admonish any of the nursing staff who 'distempered themselves in drink'.[50] Dismissals for drunkenness continued in the middle years of the nineteenth century. In 1851 two nurses from Rahere Ward and one from Abernethy Ward lost their jobs within a period of three weeks; in each case the offender was said to be intoxicated. Of course these were probably the worst offenders. Perhaps more typical was Sister Colston in the 1830s, remembered by James Paget as 'rough-tongued, scolding, not seldom rather tipsy; and yet very watchful and really very helpful, especially in what she felt to be good cases'.[51]

By the beginning of the nineteenth century the old rule that all Sisters had to have experience as a nurse had been abandoned. Indeed the difference in status between Sisters and nurses was such that promotion from nurse to Sister had become extremely rare. However in 1818 it was decided to promote some of the most active and trustworthy nurses to the rank of Sister. The experiment was successful, and in the 1830s the Charity Commissioners were given many testimonials of the good work done by those who had been promoted.[52]

One of the Sisters was singled out by Paget for special praise. This was Mary Owen, Sister Rahere, who was 'the chief among them, stout, ruddy, positive, very watchful'. She 'once taught an erring house-surgeon how to compress a posterior tibial artery; she could always report correctly the progress of a case; and from her wages she saved all she could and left it to the Hospital'. She had started her career as a nurse on Radcliffe Ward and was one of the nurses promoted to Sister in 1818. Initially on King Ward, she later served as Sister Harley and then as Sister Rahere until her death in 1848.[53] The Governors erected a memorial tablet to her in the church of St Bartholomew the Less, where it can still be seen. The tablet records that Mary Owen 'for thirtynine years faithfully and kindly discharged the duties of a nurse and Sister of the Hospital; she bequeathed the sum of £250, the chief savings of her useful life, to the Samaritan Fund attached to this Hospital, a fund . . . by which the necessities of the patients are often greatly relieved'.

In 1842 the Treasurer, James Bentley, began to award annual prizes to those Sisters and nurses whose conduct was most satisfactory and whose attention to the patients recommended them as examples to others. This was evidently found to be a useful means of encouraging higher standards among the nursing staff, for in 1848 a similar prize was established by the President of the Hospital, Matthias Prime Lucas, and in 1857 the Bentley prize was endowed on a permanent basis. Both are still awarded annually. Mary Owen

James Bentley Esqre

Donation of £1000 from

The Treasurer reported the receipt of a Cheque for One Thousand Pounds from James Bentley Esqre late Treasurer of the Hospital to be invested in the £3 per Cent Consols in Trust, the Dividends thereof to be awarded upon the Annual General View Day of the Hospital as follows:

vizt:

1st — A Prize of £10 to the House Surgeon whose kind conduct and attention to the Patients has been most exemplary during the preceding Year.

2nd — A Prize of £5 to one of the Sisters of the Hospital whose Ward has been in the most satisfactory state during the whole of the preceding year; and whose kind attention to the Patients entrusted to her care, and general conduct has been of a character to justify the Steward and the Matron in recommending her as an Example to the other Sisters.

3rd — Two Prizes of £2.10 each to two of the Nurses from different Wards whose conduct has given most satisfaction to the Matron the Sister of the Ward and Officers in the performance of their Duties and whose diligence and attention to the Poor Patients has been creditable to themselves and to the Hospital.

The remainder of the Interest to be applied in aid of the General Funds of the Hospital for the relief of the Poor

Minutes of the Board of Governors, confirming the endowment of the Bentley prize in May 1857. The prizes were to be awarded on the annual View Day when the Governors made a formal inspection of the Hospital.

was one of the first prizewinners, in 1843. Another was Mary Ann Evans, commended by Paget as Sister Hope in the 1830s, who won the Bentley prize in 1844 and again in 1858, and retired in 1860 after more than forty years' service.[54]

In 1849 London was attacked by an epidemic of cholera. By then there were numerous general hospitals in the capital, but St Bartholomew's was the first to accept cholera patients. No fewer than 478 cases were admitted to Bentley and Lucas Wards in a period of five months, and 199 of them died in the Hospital. The medical knowledge of the time could not provide a truly effective treatment for cholera, but the patients were given hot baths and ice-cold drinks and the nurses used friction to maintain their body temperature. After the epidemic the Governors expressed their gratitude to Sister Bentley and Sister Lucas 'who did not hesitate to take charge of the first patients attacked by this distressing visitation, and continued to attend most carefully and humanely'. They commended their disregard of danger and their devotion and fidelity in caring for their patients. The two Sisters were each given a gratuity of fifteen guineas, the equivalent of three or four months' salary, for their services during the epidemic.[55]

By the 1850s the Sisters at Bart's could be described as 'full of patience, experience, kindness and firmness'. Another observer called them 'intelligent and . . . devoted to their work and to the well-doing of their patients'.[56] By the 1860s, a typical nurse at the Hospital could be described as one who was 'kind and diligent in her attendance on the sick, and did rough work and laboured long hours with heroic fortitude'.[57] In 1912 Sir William Church, a former Physician to the Hospital, recalled the nurses he had known in the 1860s: Nurse Flack was 'the untidiest and most dirty-looking of women, but an excellent nurse and beloved by every patient in her ward', while Sister Abernethy was 'a typical Sister of the old school, of fine commanding presence, a strict disciplinarian, but with the kindest of hearts and a presence of mind which never deserted her'. Whatever they may have lacked in education, the nurses of this period were for the most part caring and faithful in their duties, and the era of dishonest and drunken nurses was generally acknowledged to lie in the past.[58]

During the early nineteenth century nursing salaries also showed a gradual improvement. By 1803 the Matron's salary had reached £200 a year, but the Sisters and nurses were still poorly paid: in 1814 a Sister received six or seven shillings a week, a nurse four shillings. A long-standing custom allowed each Sister to claim one shilling from every patient admitted to her ward, and a further shilling purportedly to meet the cost of earthenware supplied by her for the patient's use. A nurse could similarly claim sixpence from each patient. It seems that the Sisters and nurses had become dependent on these fees, but by 1821 the Governors were prepared to accept that the system was open to abuse and that patients could be excluded from treatment in the Hospital because of their inability to pay. In July 1821 the fees were abolished and salaries increased. Sisters were then to receive from fourteen to twentyseven shillings a week, and nurses seven shillings. Night nurses who had previously been paid sixpence per night were to receive ninepence.[59] The remuneration of the nursing staff remained at roughly this level for much of the century. In the early 1860s a Sister received eighteen

Nurses in the uniform of the mid nineteenth century. This photograph was taken c.1908–10, and shows two nurses of that era dressed in the uniform of their predecessors.

shillings a week, increasing to one guinea after fifteen years' service. Her uniform was supplied by the Hospital, but she had to provide most of her meals and furniture for her room out of her weekly pay. By 1874 a Sister's salary had increased to twentyfive or thirty shillings a week, the highest rate in any London hospital, while a nurse was paid eight or nine shillings, a figure comparable to nursing salaries elsewhere.[60]

In the early part of the century Sisters and nurses at St Bartholomew's were also given sufficient food for a dinner on Sundays at the Hospital's expense, and the nurses received half a loaf of bread and a pint of beer daily. In 1839 the Governors agreed to provide the nurses with the ingredients for a dinner every day, but this concession was not extended to the Sisters.[61] The nurses' daily allowance then consisted of one pound of bread with butter and cheese, half a pound of raw meat and twelve ounces of potatoes, together with a pint of beer. If they wanted vegetables or other items they had to supply their own. All their food was kept and cooked in the ward scullery, which also contained a water closet, sink and bath. Bart's was one of the last hospitals to abandon the practice of nurses cooking their own meals in the wards. In 1874 it was the custom for one of the nurses in each ward to act as 'kitchen nurse', which meant that she had to cook meals for the patients, the Sister, her colleagues and herself, while taking a smaller share in the general duties of the ward. Nurses ate in the scullery, while Sisters took their meals in their bedrooms adjoining the wards.[62] Another three years were to pass before the Hospital provided its nurses with regular cooked meals in a dining room.

In the wards, staff numbers continued to increase. In the sixteenth and early seventeenth centuries St Bartholomew's had employed one Sister for roughly every nine beds,[63] and the ratio was still much the same in the early eighteenth century when there were 280 beds and a nursing staff of about 32.[64] By the 1820s the number of beds had grown to 480 and the nursing staff to 100. Each of the large 'double' wards was staffed by a Sister and three nurses, the latter undertaking night duty every third night. The smaller 'single' wards were staffed by one Sister and one nurse, and relied on night nurses who came in from outside the Hospital to cover the hours of darkness. By 1837 the regular employment of night nurses had apparently been discontinued and each 'single' ward had a staff of a Sister and two nurses. There were at that time 29 Sisters and 75 nurses, and 50 of the nurses were expected to serve on the night duty rota. Nurses wore a brown uniform which distinguished them from the Sisters who wore blue.[65] In the 1860s the Hospital employed 25 Sisters and 83 nurses to serve a daily average of about 550 patients in the wards.[66]

Working hours were long, and at the beginning of the nineteenth century were probably defined only by the rule that Sisters and nurses on day duty should be in bed by 10 p.m.[67] By the 1860s all the wards were 'double', with a complement of one Sister and three nurses to every ward, and a formal timetable for the nurses had been introduced. The three were not ranked by seniority or experience but simply shared the work of the ward between them.[68] Their day began at 6 a.m., although the Sisters generally did not start work until 8.30. The nursing timetable at the end of the decade was described by a correspondent to *The Times*:

> The nurse whose duty it is to sit up, say on Monday night, rises at 6 o'clock on Monday morning, attends to the wants of her patients during the day, and performs her share of the general ward work, remaining on duty until 5 p.m., when she is at liberty to retire to rest until 10 p.m., at which hour her labours again begin and are continued without intermission until the following evening . . . On Wednesday her duties begin at 6 a.m. and terminate at 10 p.m.; the cycle [is then] resumed on Thursday morning.

This system seems to have been unique to Bart's. In other London hospitals night duty was rotated on a weekly or monthly basis, or a separate night staff was employed. At St Bartholomew's in the 1860s a nurse worked for more than twenty hours, with no opportunity to sleep in her bed, on one day in every three. She was required to be on duty for at least 48 hours out of 72, or an average of sixteen hours a day. Within those hours she was allowed time for taking her meals, and when the ward was not busy she might be permitted to rest in an armchair or find leisure for reading or needlework. At 10 a.m. on every third Sunday, and on one weekday every three weeks, she was given the rest of the day off. She had a week's paid holiday after one year's service, and two weeks after four years.[69]

The health of the nurses inevitably suffered from the conditions in which they lived and worked. In the 1830s they slept in a dormitory in a disused ward in the West Wing, but by the 1860s they were accommodated in small rooms which had been constructed around the staircases of the ward blocks, with one or two beds to each room. These rooms were dark, unheated, poorly ventilated and scarcely larger than cupboards. Living close to the wards also made the nurses highly vulnerable to infectious diseases. In the mid nineteenth century typhus and scarlet fever cases were placed in the ordinary wards of the Hospital, and patients and nurses frequently contracted fevers as a result. During the 1850s and 1860s no fewer than twenty-seven nurses died of fever in sixteen years, and of eleven Sisters attacked with fever only three recovered. In 1869 working conditions at the Hospital were

25

RULES

<small>TO BE OBSERVED BY THE</small>

SISTERS AND NURSES

<small>OF</small>

St. Bartholomew's Hospital.

ORDERED,

THAT on the Sundays the Outward Doors of the Hospital shall be open only during the Hours allowed for the Admission of Visitors.

THAT no Sister or Nurse shall go out of the Hospital to fetch Porter or other Liquor after the Outward Gates are closed.

THAT the Sisters and Nurses, before they retire to Bed (not later than Ten o'Clock every Night), shall carefully observe if any Patient be out of the Ward; and, if any Patient be absent, the Sister must give Notice thereof the next Morning to the Steward or Matron, who shall report the same to the Treasurer.

THAT no Sister or Nurse shall allow any Provisions, Beer, or other Liquor, to be brought into the Ward than those prescribed by the Physician, Surgeon, or Apothecary of the Hospital.

SISTERS or NURSES acting contrary to the foregoing Rules will be reported by the Steward or Matron to the Treasurer, in order that they may be admonished or discharged.

Rules for Sisters and nurses, c. 1860.

fiercely attacked in the press. In *The Times* one correspondent described the nurses' living quarters as 'a disgrace to humanity'. Others pointed out that, in fetching medicines from the dispensary and food from the kitchens, nurses constantly found themselves carrying heavy loads up and down the steep staircases of the ward blocks. Some could barely cope with the weight of linen which they were expected to carry to and from the laundry. It is not surprising that nurses frequently fell asleep on duty, although the Hospital authorities took the view that their hours and terms of employment were comparable to those which prevailed in domestic service.[70]

Chapter Three

THE BIRTH OF PROFESSIONAL NURSING: 1861–1910

The first stirrings of nursing reform at Bart's came shortly after the founding of the Nightingale School of Nursing at St Thomas' Hospital in 1860. The Nightingale School was a pioneer venture, with its origins in the Nightingale Fund established as a testimonial to Florence Nightingale's work in the Crimea during the 1850s. It endeavoured to train its students in the most basic elements of nursing care – moving, dressing and observing patients, the making of bandages, and so on – but was also intended to teach them sobriety, honesty, cleanliness and other moral qualities which were perceived as lacking in the untrained nurses of the day. Within a year of its opening Florence Nightingale was in communication with James Paget, the most eminent member of the medical staff at Bart's. 'To tell you the truth,' she wrote, 'I look to . . . all hospitals making themselves into nursing schools; why not, just as much as medical schools?'. She sent Paget full details of the Nightingale School, and commented: 'With regard to the nursing school, I am delighted to hear what [St Bartholomew's] means to do', adding that she would be happy to review any scheme which the Hospital might draw up. Paget and Nightingale remained in communication through the early months of 1861, but their surviving correspondence fails to make clear precisely what plans were being made. In the event nothing came of the scheme, and Bart's continued to function without a training school for a further sixteen years. 'Mine has always been an unrequited love for St Bartholomew's', Nightingale wrote to Paget; 'I have worshipped that saint [but] he has never taken any notice of me'.[1]

In 1865 the Hospital appointed a new Matron, Frances Drake, and in 1866 a new Clerk to the Governors, William Henry Cross. It was perhaps as a result of their interest that the first 'scrubbers' were employed in 1868, to relieve the nurses of the task of cleaning the floors of the wards and staircases. The scrubbers were 'daily women' who came in from outside the Hospital. They worked from 7 a.m. until 11 a.m. and were required to scour the wards twice weekly. Nurses were still expected to clean the grates and all the furniture, to cook Sister's meals, light the fires and wash the patients' dishes, and to sweep the wards early in the morning before the arrival of the scrubbers; but the Governors expressed a hope that when nurses were no

St Bartholomew's Hospital in 1870.

longer required to clean the floors, the Hospital would be able to recruit many women who had previously been discouraged from offering their services.[2] In 1870 the nurses' sleeping accommodation was enlarged by converting the two small rooms off each ward into one larger room, and the daily rotation of night duty was replaced by a weekly rotation in which one week of night duty was followed by two weeks of daytime work. The Governors' intention was to enable every nurse, whether on day or night duty, to have at least eight consecutive hours' rest in the course of every 24 hours.[3]

These changes made for better working conditions, but the nurses remained effectively untrained. A survey undertaken by supporters of Florence Nightingale in 1874–5 reported that several London hospitals claimed to train young women as nurses, yet most did little more than place them in the wards to learn what they could from observation and practice.[4] St Bartholomew's made no claim to offer training of any kind. However an impetus for further change came when the noted philanthropist Sir Sydney Waterlow became Treasurer of the Hospital in the summer of 1874. Waterlow was an admirer of the work of Florence Nightingale and in the early 1870s as chairman of the Central London Sick Asylum District Board had called on her assistance in finding trained nurses for a new infirmary at Highgate. Within two years of his appointment as Treasurer, Waterlow had resolved to establish a school of nursing at Bart's in order to supply the

Hospital with trained nurses of its own.[5] In April 1876 the Governors approved a scheme for the training of nurses and allocated the sum of £100 for the expenses of the school in its first year. The scheme was to start in 1877, and the details were framed by the Clerk to the Governors, W. H. Cross. Following the practice at St Thomas' Hospital and elsewhere the pupils were to be known as probationers. They were to attend for twelve months during which they would be given 'regular instruction in the technical knowledge of nursing'. Their salary for the year was to be £10, which was only half the sum paid to the regular nursing staff: the Governors evidently had an eye to economy as well as the improvement of nursing standards. One probationer was to be attached to each ward, but could be relocated at the Matron's discretion if the work of the Hospital required it. At the end of the year the probationers would receive a certificate of competency, if they had discharged their duties to the satisfaction of the Hospital authorities and the medical staff.[6]

The new trainees were given a distinctive uniform. Nurses who were not probationers continued to wear the old uniform, a brown woollen dress which was said to be 'excellently fitted for concealing dirt', with an apron and any cap which the nurse cared to choose, or no cap at all; but the probationers wore dark grey cotton, and small caps to a standard pattern. The new uniform was cleaner and neater than that worn by the old nurses, though it was also designed – in the opinion of one of the medical staff – to allow its wearers no personal vanity.[7] Later it was noted that grey had been the colour worn by the medieval Sisters, but it is not certain whether any historical allusion was intended when the colour of the new probationers' uniform was chosen.

Other changes were made at the same time. The weekly rota for night duty was abolished. Each nurse was now to act as day nurse in her ward for two months, followed by two months as night nurse. Night Superintendents were also appointed to visit the wards at night and to oversee the work of the night nurses. The staffing of each ward was increased from four to five persons: Sister, day nurse, night nurse, probationer and ward assistant. The ward assistants (or ward maids, as they came to be known) were to reside in the Hospital. They were to do some of the cleaning and cooking in the wards and fetch and carry items from the kitchen, laundry and dispensary. Scrubbers were still to be employed to clean the staircases, though the scrubbing of the ward floors was to be taken over by the ward maids.[8] In theory the nurses were no longer expected to undertake the most menial work, but in practice the ward maids were unable to relieve them of all heavy duties and the nurses found that they still had floors to sweep, lockers and tables to scrub and baths to clean.[9]

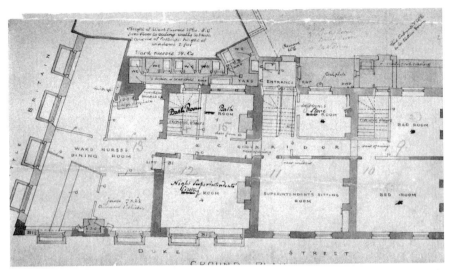

Plan of the nurses' home, 1877. It stood on or near the site later occupied by the Nurses' Gate in Little Britain.

Accommodation for the night nurses, ward assistants and some of the probationers was provided in the Hospital's first nurses' home, which was established in 1877 in three converted houses by Little Britain. The day nurses and most of the probationers were accommodated in the old nurses' rooms adjoining the ward staircases. Although each room now housed only two people instead of three, the old nurses' quarters remained cramped and ill-ventilated and were not swept away until the end of the century. The Sisters still ate on the wards, and the nurses were still expected to take some of their meals there, but the arrangements for the new nurses' home included the opening of the Hospital's first dining rooms, where a breakfast and a cooked dinner for all nurses were provided daily.[10]

Frances Drake was still Matron when the training scheme began. She was the widow of a solicitor and was not, of course, a trained nurse, but had come to Bart's with some previous experience at the Foundling Hospital.[11] A history of nursing published in 1906 said that 'Mrs Drake . . . sympathised with the new movement and helped it by all means in her power',[12] but it is far from clear whether she was really in sympathy with the changes that had been introduced. Her attitude to nurses was that they were in effect servants, even if they might be allowed better wages and more liberty than was usually permitted to domestic servants in private life. She expected them to carry heavy loads like servant girls and dismissed one nurse whose sole offence was to complain to the Treasurer about the weight she had to carry. The idea

31

that nursing might be a career for 'ladies' was abhorrent to her and she tried to discourage applicants who did not have a traditional working-class background.[13] When Sir Sydney Waterlow introduced his reforms she was over sixty years of age and may well have been less than wholehearted in her enthusiasm for change.

The first pupils arrived on 1 May 1877. There were fourteen of them, their ages varying from 21 to 33. One of the first entrants later recalled that 'there was no entrance examination [but] we all arrived one morning and proceeded to put on our uniform . . . in the afternoon we attended a lecture by Dr Duckworth'.[14] Dyce Duckworth was Assistant Physician to the Hospital, and in his lecture he stressed the need for nurses to be observant, truthful and even-tempered, to cultivate good habits of punctuality and cleanliness and to obey orders without questioning. Remembering the failings of some of the older nurses, he also felt obliged to warn the probationers to take alcoholic drinks only at mealtimes and to resort to tea or cocoa on occasions of special need. Something of the influence of Florence Nightingale can be seen in his exhortation that no duty or trouble should be too much for them: they should devote themselves wholly to labour on behalf of the sick and never think that they were overworked or unfairly treated.[15] A few of the older nurses and Sisters attended the lecture but most seem to have stayed away; many medical students went, perhaps out of curiosity.[16]

Although by 1877 there were one or two Sisters at Bart's who had attended the Nightingale School at St Thomas' Hospital, the great majority were untrained and neither they nor the Matron were able to offer any teaching to the newly arrived probationers. Nursing textbooks scarcely existed and the only available lecturers were those members of the medical staff who were sympathetic to the cause of nurse training. The Board of Governors had therefore appointed Duckworth and his colleague Alfred Willett, Assistant Surgeon, to act as instructors to the probationers. They each drew up a syllabus of lectures and practical demonstrations. Duckworth proposed to cover the elements of physiology, hygiene, diet, the treatment of acute and chronic disease, medical emergencies, modes of death, the use of medicaments and apparatus, and nursing conduct and discipline; while Willett intended to deal with elementary anatomy and surgery, the treatment of accidents and post-operative cases, surgical nursing and surgical emergencies.[17] Impressive though this programme appears, the tuition provided by the Hospital was fairly rudimentary. Duckworth or Willett gave a lecture or practical demonstration every week, but apart from this one weekly session there was no formal curriculum. Each probationer was attached to a ward and was left very largely to fend for herself.

In later life Matilda Jenkins, who was one of the first intake of probationers, gave an account of her experiences in her first days at St Bartholomew's, where she had been assigned to Harley Ward in the East Wing:

One day a sweep was brought into Harley with six fractured ribs. 'Pro,' said Sister, 'go and wash that patient'. I had never been shown how to set about such a task, and his hair alone, which was full of soot, nearly drove me to despair. Another day I was ordered to give soap–and–water injections to the same man, and also to a man with a compound fracture of the femur. I had never given one before, and had no instructions whatever given to me. I was in tears before I had finished, and so, I fear, were the patients.[18]

Nevertheless the probationers learnt what they could. Duckworth took such an interest in them that they were called 'Ducky's lambs'. He took them into his wards and gave lessons on bedmaking or on 'the contents of the doctor's cupboard'. Willett taught them bandaging and the use of splints. Further unofficial tuition was provided by junior doctors and even by the medical students. One of them showed Matilda Jenkins how to take a temperature, although this was not then considered a suitable task for a nurse, and Jenkins recalled that 'there was generally a row' if a Sister caught one of the probationers using a thermometer.[18]

Patients who had undergone an operation were expected to need one, two or even three months for their wounds to heal before convalescence. Until the 1870s the dressing of wounds was undertaken by the younger doctors and medical students, and in particular by senior students who were known as 'dressers'. All wounds were expected and encouraged to suppurate, since infection was thought to be part of the normal healing process. Duckworth showed the first probationers how to make poultices and they spent much of their time doing this. In a surgical ward it was not unusual for thirty to be needed in a single day. Because the dressings were non–absorbent, they had to be changed two or three times daily, and this became an important part of the probationers' duties. Antiseptic techniques, which were to end the need for constant changing of poultices, were not brought into full use at Bart's until after 1880.[19]

The scheme of training approved by the Governors in 1876 does not seem to have allowed for an end-of-year examination, but in fact an examination did take place when the first batch of probationers finished their training in the spring of 1878, and certificates were awarded on the basis of the results. Of the fourteen probationers who had entered St Bartholomew's in May

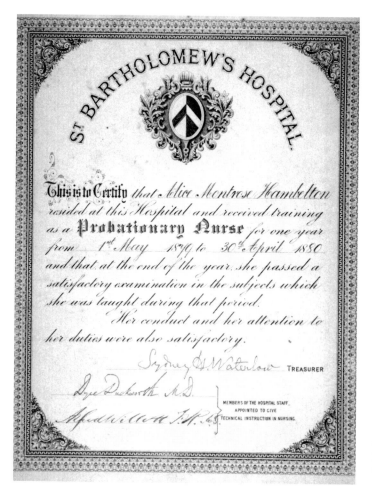

*Certificate
awarded after one
year's training as
a probationer,
1880.*

1877, ten sat the examination and seven passed. Permanent posts were offered to the successful candidates, but most refused them because of the conditions in the wards. Five left the Hospital, though Matilda Jenkins later returned. Of the two who stayed on, one took up an appointment as a staff nurse; the other became Night Superintendent and was promoted to Sister a few months later.[20]

In 1878 the Governors asked Frances Drake to resign to make room for a Matron who was a trained nurse. They resolved that her successor would have a new title of 'Matron and Superintendent of Nursing' and that an Assistant Matron would be appointed to take charge of the linen and bedding, so that the Matron might have more time to supervise the work and training of the nurses.[21] Drake agreed to retire and was granted a pension by the Hospital, but the vacancy does not seem to have been advertised; instead Sir Sydney Waterlow approached Florence Nightingale and Henry Bonham Carter, Secretary of the Nightingale Fund, to seek their help in finding a suitable candidate.[22]

They responded by recommending Maria Machin, who had trained at St Thomas' Hospital in 1873 and had made a profound impression there. The Nightingale School wrote a superb report on her as a nurse 'of altogether superior education . . . highest character and most spiritual tone and purpose . . . experienced in life and . . . unflinching in resolution'. She had won this reputation in a surprisingly short time. She had been a probationer for only nine months, during which she had been ill for 53 days, and her attendance in the ward had been irregular because of a septic finger.[23] After leaving the Nightingale School she had worked as Sister in charge of the nurses' home at St Thomas', and then went to Canada to be Lady Superintendent of the Montreal General Hospital. She reformed many of its nursing practices in Nightingale fashion and attempted to set up a nursing school but some of the Hospital managers were dissatisfied with the changes which she had wished to make.[24] She in turn felt that they had 'broken faith' with her,[25] resigned her post in Montreal and returned to England, intending to work at St Bartholomew's.

Maria Machin was a devoted follower of Florence Nightingale, with whom she corresponded regularly. Like many of the new breed of nurses who took their inspiration from Nightingale, Machin felt a deep conviction that her calling was a religious one, and she stated her belief that 'God should be the acknowledged standard . . . in our sisterhood of nursing'. In Montreal she had sometimes been uncertain of her suitability for a managerial role. 'I often wish I were a Ward Sister instead of Superintendent', she wrote in 1877, 'I'm so much happier nursing the sick than governing the [nurses] who are well'.[26] Her first reaction to the prospect of becoming Matron at Bart's was to say that 'such a work would be far beyond my powers'. She initially welcomed the proposal, apparently put to her through Florence Nightingale, that she should have a trial period as a Sister or Night Superintendent before becoming Matron. In the autumn of 1878 she wrote to Henry Bonham Carter, saying that she was still nervous 'about assuming a work of such difficulty' but would take the position of Matron if it were offered to her. She felt that in accepting such a demanding post she would have to rely heavily on the support of Bonham Carter and of Nightingale, whom she asked to 'watch for me and over me, and direct [me] from without'. However she changed her mind about the trial period and took up the appointment as Matron in December 1878, at the age of 37.[27]

Machin wished to instil the principles of the Nightingale School into St Bartholomew's and brought some of the Nightingale-trained nurses who had worked with her in Canada to fill vacant Sisters' posts at Bart's.[28] She raised the minimum age for probationers from 20 to 23 and increased the length of training from one year to two. Although the salary for first-year probationers was further reduced, to £8, second-years were to be paid £12.[29] In 1880 one of the Surgeons, William Savory, informed Florence Nightingale that Machin had improved the character of the probationary nurses and that their work had become more satisfactory; his senior colleague James Paget said that she was well esteemed by all the medical staff and told Nightingale that 'the changes already made for the better are far more than could have been expected ten or fifteen years ago'.[30] However Paget advised caution, fearing that she could arouse opposition if she tried to act too quickly. He was a shrewd judge of the situation. Machin had become impatient because of her inability to make changes as rapidly as she wished. In November 1879 she was complaining about the little that she had been able to achieve after almost a year in office. The Hospital authorities, she wrote, 'prefer gradual improvement to radical reforms'. The Treasurer was often too busy to see her, the untrained Sisters were obstructive, and she could not persuade them to change their traditional ways of doing things. She sent her letter of resignation in January 1881 after little more than two years as Matron.[31]

Her successor was Ethel Gordon Manson, who was later to marry Dr Bedford Fenwick and to achieve deserved fame as the pioneer of state registration. Born in Scotland in 1857, she had spent eighteen months as a probationer, first at the Children's Hospital, Nottingham, and then at the Manchester Royal Infirmary. In September 1879 she became a Sister at the London Hospital, whence she successfully applied for the post of Matron at Bart's.[32] Her background was very different to that of Maria Machin, and her appointment has sometimes been seen as a conscious decision by St Bartholomew's to break with the Nightingale tradition. She had no links to the Nightingale circle and in later life fought to take the professionalisation of nursing far beyond the limits that Florence Nightingale found acceptable. However it is far from certain that her thinking had developed to this stage when she was first appointed to St Bartholomew's, for she was then only 24 years of age. Ethel Manson was almost certainly the youngest Matron the Hospital has ever had; indeed some of the senior medical staff objected to her appointment on the grounds that she was too young and too attractive. However Sir Sydney Waterlow had already received good reports of her and had paid discreet visits to her ward at the London Hospital to inspect her methods of working. He was impressed by

Ethel Gordon Manson, Matron 1881–87, afterwards Mrs Bedford Fenwick.

her evident determination and the toughness of character that would enable
her to take on a job of the utmost difficulty. At her interview with Waterlow
she was asked 'if she thought she could manage the old Sisters', and she
convinced the Treasurer that she was not afraid of anyone. She was initially
appointed for a trial period of six months, but in December 1881 Waterlow
reported to the Governors that she had been found highly suitable and she
was confirmed in her post with an initial salary of £250 per annum.[33]

Ethel Manson's determination enabled her to succeed where Machin had
failed. In later years she was remembered as someone who had 'swept
through the Hospital like a whirlwind'.[34] She spent three hours every
morning, and two hours every evening, visiting each ward in turn to ensure
that cleanliness and efficiency were maintained.[35] She insistently demanded
the highest standards from her nurses and was an indefatigable campaigner
for improvements in their training and working conditions. She formalised
the system, already partly effective under her predecessor, whereby
candidates were accepted for training only after working for at least one
month as 'extra nurses' (or, as they became known, 'probationers on trial').
Detailed reports on the progress of all probationers were started in May
1881, her first month at St Bartholomew's. A structured teaching plan was
introduced. Probationers gained their ward experience by working in
different wards in rotation, spending three months in each of four wards in
their first year. In 1882 the course was extended to three years, with
examinations at the end of the first and third years. The salary for
probationers in their third year was to be £5 per quarter; if not handsomely
rewarded, they were at any rate to receive no less than the old untrained
nurses had been paid. Manson was the first Matron to participate in the
marking of the nurses' examinations, for which the medical staff previously
had sole responsibility. From 1885 gold medals and book prizes, sponsored
by the Clothworkers' Company, were awarded to the best candidates in each
examination.[36]

Where she found old and ill-advised practices, such as getting patients out
of bed before 6 a.m., or making them help with bedmaking, Manson
insisted that such behaviour should cease.[37] She wanted to see
St Bartholomew's staffed entirely with trained nurses. By the time she left
the Hospital most of the untrained Sisters and nurses had been weeded out,
though a few of the better ones remained in office (and indeed the last
untrained Sister did not retire until 1907).[38] Nevertheless the Matron's policy
meant that there were remarkable promotion opportunities for the best of
the qualified nurses. Hannah Turner, the first gold medallist, was made a
Ward Sister within two months of completing her training, and many of her
contemporaries received almost equally rapid advancement.[39]

The Sisters of St Bartholomew's Hospital, c.1885. Ethel Manson, Matron, in centre of photograph.

As a disciplinarian and a reformer, Ethel Manson was determined that her high standards should be reflected in the uniforms worn by her staff. Previously the Sisters had worn blue dresses without caps or aprons; each dress was made of blue french merino, but the pattern was left to the Sisters' discretion.[40] Manson asked the Hospital to supply frilled caps and strapless aprons 'for such of the Sisters as were willing to wear them' and effectively persuaded all the Sisters to wear an identical uniform. She wanted every Sister to be precisely dressed, with not a button out of place, and is said to have personally measured 'every yard of cap frilling' to ensure that it was exactly correct.[41] Another change was in the uniform of the staff nurses. In 1881 she introduced caps of a standard design to be worn by all nurses, and in due course the old brown dresses were phased out because the trained nurses objected to wearing them. The certificated nurses and probationers in their second and third years were given a uniform similar to that of the first-year probationers, but of blue and white striped material instead of plain grey. Their caps were similar to those worn by the Sisters, with strings tied under the chin, but their aprons were of a different design with straps at the shoulders. Staff nurses wore a blue belt, the second-year and third-year probationers a white one.[42]

The women who came to the Hospital for training in Ethel Manson's time were not recruited exclusively from the local employment market, as the old nurses seem to have been. Of the 26 probationers who started their training in 1881, Manson's first year in office, twelve gave London addresses; of the rest, ten came from the English provinces, one from Wales, two from Scotland and one from the Netherlands. Their backgrounds were remarkably varied. Six had previous nursing experience of one kind or another, seven had been in domestic service and one was formerly a teacher in a Board School. Others were evidently from middle-class families. Two candidates had been employed as governesses and there were several young ladies in their twenties who had no previous work experience. The Hospital was willing to train the daughters of cowkeepers and carpenters, farmers and clergymen, surgeons and solicitors.[43]

In 1884, however, a distinction was introduced. Manson began a scheme whereby 'ladies desirous of acquiring some practical knowledge of nursing' could become 'special probationers' for three months on payment of a fee. The scheme was similar to those which already existed at several other London hospitals, although the term 'special probationer' was unique to Bart's.[44] The intention was to attract ladies of a superior class, who were presumed to want neither the meagre salaries paid to the ordinary probationers nor the commitment to three years of hard work in the wards. Sir James Paget remarked that in his youth 'the admission of young ladies to be nurses in this or any similar hospital' would have been thought scandalous, yet in the event it proved wholly acceptable. As was to be expected, the special probationers had various privileges: they did not live with the other nurses, but were accommodated separately in King Square, Finsbury. They were excused night duty and were allowed a later start to the working day, coming on duty at 8 or 8.30 instead of 7 a.m. Nevertheless every special probationer was informed that strict punctuality and obedience were required, and rules were drawn up reminding the young ladies that they were forbidden certain activities to which they might have thought themselves entitled. Writing lettters, receiving friends, reading novels and doing fancy work were prohibited while they were on duty, and the wearing of jewellery or high heels and curled or fringed hairstyles were all disallowed.[45] In fact many of the special probationers acquired a real interest in hospital nursing, and at the end of their three-month contracts chose to remain at Bart's as ordinary probationers. By the end of the decade St Bartholomew's seems to have become the most socially acceptable of all the London hospitals for young ladies from professional backgrounds who wished to train as nurses. It could claim to have the daughters of a Duke and of a former Lord Mayor of London among its special probationers; and its regular probationers included daughters of architects, accountants and stockbrokers, military officers and lawyers, who had sought training with the intention of entering a nursing career.[46]

Another of Manson's innovations was the Trained Nurses Institution, founded in 1886. Its object was to supply the middle-class public with Bart's-trained nurses, on payment of an appropriate fee. The Governors expected that within three years of its foundation the Institution would return a profit; at the same time they hoped that it would attract more women to train as probationers. Originally the Hospital took the fees and paid the nurses a salary, but in 1906 an alternative arrangement was introduced whereby the nurses were allowed to keep the fees and pay a percentage to the Hospital. The Institution survived until 1948 but the numbers of nurses joining it declined rapidly in its last few years.[47]

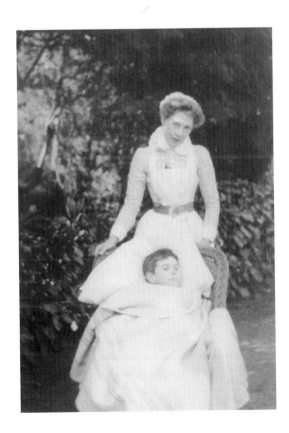

A nurse from the Trained Nurses Institution, with a young patient, c.1904.

In March 1887 Ethel Manson left the Hospital to be married. By then the reputation of the training course was such that 1500 enquiries were received in a year, although there were only about fifty vacancies.[48] Mrs Bedford Fenwick, as she was thenceforth known, went on to begin her thirty-year campaign for state registration of trained nurses.[49] At St Bartholomew's her successor Isla Stewart also took up this cause, and the Hospital became a bastion of the struggle for registration. From Mrs Bedford Fenwick Bart's inherited a commitment to a three-year professional training and a belief that nursing was a career for intelligent women of any social class. Fenwick and Stewart worked together to establish nursing as a closed profession, and found themselves in opposition both to the managements of other hospitals, who saw the registration movement as an attack on their powers of control over their nurses, and also to the followers of Florence Nightingale, to whom nursing was a quasi-religious vocation for which one or two years of training seemed wholly adequate.

Like her predecessor Isla Stewart had been born in Scotland. She had attended the Nightingale School and had been appointed a Sister at St Thomas' Hospital after only nine months as a probationer. In 1885 she became Matron of the emergency smallpox camp run by the Metropolitan Asylums Board at Darenth in Kent, and in the following year the Board moved her to Hackney as Matron of the Homerton Fever Hospital, which later became the Eastern Hospital. In 1887 she wrote to her mother that 'the biggest appointment in the nursing world is vacant, [and] I am going to have a try for it'. Her application was successful and she began work as Matron of St Bartholomew's in June 1887 at the age of thirty.[50]

Under her guidance new regulations for the training of nurses were issued in 1893. Probationers on appointment were to be aged between 23 and 35. An elementary examination was devised, to be sat by all candidates before they were accepted as probationers on trial. At the end of their trial period they were to appear in person before the Matron, the Clerk to the Governors and representatives of the medical staff, and if their performance was felt to be satisfactory they could be formally elected as probationers. Salaries were confirmed at £2 per quarter in the first year, £3 in the second and £5 in the third, with full board and lodging provided throughout. After passing the examination at the end of her first year a trainee became known as a 'staff probationer', in recognition of her partial competence; after passing the final examination in her third year she was awarded the Hospital's certificate and became a staff nurse. Under a new rule introduced in 1893, she was obliged to work at St Bartholomew's for at least one year after gaining her certificate, but could leave if she wished at the end of her fourth year.[51]

In the early 1890s the probationer's working day began at 7 a.m. and did

Isla Stewart, Matron 1887–1910, photographed outside the West Wing in 1907.

not finish until supper. Her time off was taken in periods of a few hours on certain days during the working week. After three or six months on day duty she would expect to spend three months working at night, her hours then being from 9 p.m. to 9.20 a.m. The system thus provided a double complement of nurses at work in the early hours of the morning, the busiest time in the wards, when the patients were fed and washed, the beds made and everything put in order before the arrival of the medical staff. Sisters began work at 8 a.m. On alternate days they came off duty at 6 p.m. but on

A 'staff probationer' wearing her striped uniform with a white belt and the badge of the Hospital. Photograph taken in the early 1890s.

others they worked for as long as was necessary, generally finishing at about 9 p.m. A communal dinner for the Sisters had been introduced, presumably in an attempt to reduce the isolation that must have been felt when each Sister took all her meals alone. Nurses and probationers had fixed times for every meal, but apart from their dinner at 5 p.m. the Sisters still ate in their wards and had no defined eating hours, taking their meals when they could.[52]

Although the working day was long, in her early years as Matron Isla Stewart felt that she could defend the Hospital against those who accused it of exploiting its workforce. She wrote an account of her nurses' day for *Murray's Magazine* in 1890:

> Nurses go on duty at 7 a.m., and for the next three hours they really work hard, making beds, scrubbing lockers, sweeping, polishing, dusting, and doing the hundred-and-one things that produce that air of comfort and cleanliness so characteristic of a well-kept hospital. After

A ward scene, c.1892.

10 o'clock there is a considerable pause. The patients having been well attended to are rarely in want of anything, and the nurses now have leisure to do a little sewing or other ward work . . . At noon the nurses go to dinner, and at 12.30 the patients' dinner is usually served. Then the ward is tidied up and made ready for the visiting Physician or Surgeon, who always produces a pleasurable excitement as he goes from bed to bed, followed by his class of students. Tea for the patients is served at 4 p.m. and for the nurses at 4.30 p.m. Then follows a very quiet time till 6 p.m., when a sort of miniature repetition of the morning's work is done. All being finished at 8p.m., the gas is turned down and the nurses wait in quietness until 9 o'clock when, on the arrival of the night nurses, they go off to supper . . . There are times when they work hard all day and have hardly a moment to sit down, but I know also there are times when they have not even so much to do as I have stated . . . Looked at in this light, the fourteen hours' work does not seem such a hardship.

She also responded to criticism of the amount of domestic labour required of nurses, and particularly of probationers:

Some nurses complain that they have to dust and sweep, and do other household work, which could be more quickly and efficiently performed by less well-educated women . . . If it be true that absolute cleanliness is a most essential factor in the recovery of a patient . . . then I think that housemaids' work is an important part of a nurse's training . . . The best nurses, in realising the necessity of cleanliness, do not wish to escape from the occasional hardness implied by it.[53]

Members of the nursing staff needed few reminders of their lowly status in the hierarchy of the Hospital. In the earlier part of the century Sisters and nurses had been expected to curtsey to the Physicians and Surgeons, and probationers were still required to remain standing in the presence of housemen.[54] In 1895 Sir Dyce Duckworth told a gathering of nurses that their job was 'to carry out the doctor's orders with implicit obedience and exactitude; if [a nurse] has any opinions, she should keep them to herself'.[55]

Training was intended to make nurses proficient in the practical tasks which were expected of them. Probationers entering the Hospital in the 1890s attended lectures by the Matron on such subjects as bedmaking, preparing patients for operation, washing patients in bed and administration of enemas. Her lectures also introduced them to basic medical terminology, invalid cookery, techniques in the cleaning of instruments and best practice in keeping medicines and lotions in the wards. Lectures on medical and surgical nursing were given to second-year and third-year probationers by the members of the medical staff who had been appointed as instructors.[56]

Lectures in bacteriology were started in 1903, at a time when the importance of asepsis in surgery was beginning to be fully understood. In 1906 Isla Stewart introduced a revised curriculum, with first-year classes on practical nursing (by the Matron, with help from the Sisters) and physiology (by a lecturer from the Medical School attached to the Hospital). In their second year the probationers were still to attend the instructors' lectures on medical and surgical nursing. In the third year there would be lectures on bacteriology, by the Hospital Pathologist, and on gynaecological and ophthalmic nursing, by the Sisters of the relevant wards. This was the first time that the Sisters had been given a formal role in teaching. By a strange irony, the ophthalmic lectures were to be given by Mary Davies, the Sister of the eye ward, who was the last untrained nurse on the staff of the Hospital. Although she lacked a formal qualification, Mary Davies was undoubtedly

46

a competent Ward Sister: the Ophthalmic Surgeon, Bowater Vernon, said of her that what she did not know about eyes was not worth knowing.[57]

Throughout this period lectures were given in the evening, roughly once a week, and it was still assumed that the major part of a nurse's education would be acquired from practical work in the wards. Isla Stewart firmly believed that ward experience was more important than theoretical teaching,[58] and in 1908 the Hospital ratified this view, by deciding that certificates would no longer be issued at the end of the three years of formal training, but only after the completion of the obligatory fourth year as a staff nurse.[59]

Nurses in their fourth and any subsequent years of service as a staff nurse were popularly known as 'blue belts', although the term 'going into blue' meant donning the traditional blue uniform of a Sister. Isla Stewart insisted that no staff nurse could be appointed without three years' training, and no Sister until she had completed the fourth year. The training scheme had been established to provide skilled nurses to fill these posts, but both Maria Machin and Mrs Bedford Fenwick had found it necessary to recruit Sisters from outside the Hospital. However by Isla Stewart's time the success of the scheme had created an ample supply of competent nurses who had been trained at Bart's, and when posts fell vacant external candidates were never considered.[60]

Many of the women who qualified at St Bartholomew's did not wish to continue working in the Hospital, and a considerable number found that a Bart's certificate gave access to career opportunities in the wider world. Some left to enter private nursing or to take up senior posts at other hospitals in England or abroad. Thus in 1887 the first gold medallist Hannnah Turner, despite her relatively humble background as a grocer's daughter, was able to secure a position as Matron at Pendlebury Children's Hospital in Lancashire.[61] Lucy Walker and Caroline Milne were trained at St Bartholomew's from 1888 to 1891 and then went to Philadelphia where they reorganised the Presbyterian Hospital Training School following the educational model which they had known at Bart's.[62] Catharine Loch, the pioneer of skilled nursing in British military hospitals in India, had been a Sister under Mrs Bedford Fenwick, and several of her fellow workers in the Indian Nursing Service were nurses who held the Bart's certificate.[63]

There were others, a smaller proportion of the total, who chose to remain at St Bartholomew's for a lifetime of service or to return there after a period of work elsewhere. Jane Skillman became a Sister in 1884 and continued in post for 26 years, .while her near contemporaries Alice Shrives (Sister Paget) and Mabel Sleigh (Sister Lucas) also served for 20 years or more.[64] Those who stayed as Ward Sisters generally developed a working relationship over a long period with the members of the medical staff who had beds in the ward. When Alfred Willett retired from the staff of the Hospital in 1902 he recalled that for more than 20 years his surgical beds had been in Pitcairn, President and Harley Wards, and that he had worked closely with the same three Sisters for practically the whole of that time. He commended all three for the length of their service, their quiet devotion to duty and the energy and conscientiousness which they brought to their work. Isla Stewart's greatest sympathies were reserved for women such as these. 'Notwithstanding the hard work,' she wrote, 'there is no life, I think, happier than that of a nurse in a hospital to which a medical school is attached. The interest in the work is so acute, the life around so changing . . . To be Sister of a ward, where the hearts of her patients do safely trust her, and where she feels herself the trusted colleague of her Surgeon or Physician – that is happiness indeed'.[65]

Rates of pay for nursing staff at Bart's were generally set at a higher level than in other London hospitals, reflecting both the larger resources of

A Sister's room, 1899.

Nurse Edith Agg returning to her ward after receiving news of her appointment as Sister Elizabeth, 1903.

St Bartholomew's and an assertion of its status as the premier hospital in England. During Stewart's years as Matron the salaries of trained nurses were rapidly increased. While Sisters' salaries remained almost unchanged from the 1870s until 1919, the pay of a newly trained nurse was increased by fifty per cent between 1890 and 1893. By the end of the nineteenth century a fourth-year nurse earnt £30, a fifth-year £35, and nurses in their sixth and subsequent years were paid £40 per annum. A Sister received about £65 on appointment and £85 after fifteen years' service.[66]

At the same time the working hours were reduced: in 1877 probationers had been on duty for fifteen hours a day, with four hours off each week and a half day once a fortnight, but by 1907 this had been reduced to an average working day of nine hours, with three days off per month.[67] For the daily work of the wards the Hospital had become heavily dependent on nurses in training, with probationers comprising about 70% of the nursing workforce.[68] The predominantly middle-aged workforce of the earlier part of the century had been replaced by one comprised largely of women in their twenties. The total numbers of staff nurses and probationers grew from 158 in 1889, shortly after Stewart's arrival, to an establishment of 250 twenty years later. St Bartholomew's then had more beds and a larger nursing staff than any of the leading hospitals in the metropolis with the exception of the

London Hospital in Whitechapel. In 1907 it claimed to employ one nurse for every 2.75 beds, a level of staffing roughly comparable to that in most of the voluntary hospitals in the capital and considerably better than in the poor-law infirmaries.[69]

A typical ward at that time had a ward maid and five daytime nursing staff – Sister, staff nurse and three probationers – and two further probationers who worked at night. No trained staff were on duty in the ward during the hours of darkness, but the Night Superintendents visited each ward at least three times in the course of the night, and in cases of emergency a Sister could be woken as she slept in her room next to the ward.[70]

Specialist nursing posts began to be established in Isla Stewart's time. When she came to Bart's there were only three nurses in the casualty department, all elderly and infirm, and two in the out-patient rooms. The first 'Sister Surgery' was appointed in 1889, with further nurses to assist her, and by 1907 the out-patient department had a staff of one Sister and 22 nurses.[71] A similar change occurred in the operating theatres. In the 1860s, and for many years after, the single theatre was looked after by Sister Lucas and Sister Abernethy whose wards adjoined it; no other nursing staff were attached to the theatre and at operations a nurse from the patient's ward attended each case. The same arrangement still prevailed in 1887 but by the beginning of the twentieth century there were two theatres worked by two trained nurses and one probationer. A 'Sister Theatre' was first appointed in 1905 when new theatres were opened, and by 1908 she had a staff of ten nurses.[72]

From her earliest years as Matron, Isla Stewart rejected the sentimental view of nursing adopted by some of the disciples of Florence Nightingale. Stewart maintained that nurses were women who had chosen, or were obliged, to take up a profession by which they could support themselves. She wrote in 1890 that:

The pedestal which nurses occupy in the eyes of many people, who adorn them with a halo of sentiment and look upon them as models of self-sacrifice, is a purely imaginary one. It has been the fashion to speak and think of a nurse's life as a beautiful renunciation of the world and worldly pleasures, the devotion of a life to soothing the dying and consoling the living . . . This is a mistake. Self-sacrifice is not a leading characteristic . . . Nurses are hard-working women who as a rule sleep soundly [and] eat heartily . . . A nurse's position towards the world is that of a woman wishing for independence, willing by her own hands to obtain and maintain it, and to have a profession, the proceeds of which will maintain her in comparative comfort, owing no man

Sister Surgery at work in the Out-patients Building, early twentieth century.

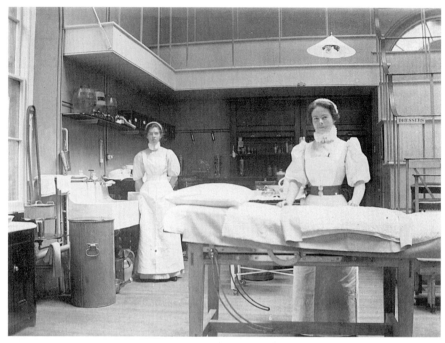

Two nurses in the operating theatre, 1904.

anything and wishing for no undeserved praise or blame. Her position towards the hospital is purely commercial. She receives board, lodging and a small salary in return for work done . . . Her position towards her patients is practically that of an attendant paid by the hospital to wait upon them and to do everything in her power for their comfort and well-being . . . Nurses, then, are literally working women, bound to give their best efforts to the institution which pays them for their work.

The nurses whom she most admired were those who combined a regard for their own financial independence with a professional commitment to the care of patients:

There are women who in taking up nursing, often as a means of livelihood, do so with the highest motives, and who in rendering themselves independent have at the same time the great pleasure of helping others. From this class come all our best Sisters and nurses.[73]

These convictions naturally led her to seek wider recognition of the professional status of nurses, and she soon became known as a protagonist in the struggle for state registration. When Isla Stewart was appointed to Bart's she did not know Mrs Bedford Fenwick, but their first meetings apparently convinced her of the need for registration and the two women rapidly became close friends as well as political allies.[74] In the early years of the registration movement Stewart was the only Matron of a leading London hospital to give it public support, and during her term of office St Bartholomew's gained a reputation as the most progressive of all the great hospitals for its nursing policy. In 1894 she convened a gathering of hospital Matrons in the Great Hall at Bart's, where she inaugurated one of the first professional nursing bodies, the Matrons' Council. Five years later another meeting at St Bartholomew's, in the Matron's house, led to the foundation of the International Council of Nurses, the first international organisation for nurses or indeed for professional women of any kind.[75]

Stewart believed that effective nursing education could not be limited to the confines of a single hospital, or even a single country. At a time when most Matrons were opposed to cooperative training, she persuaded the Governors of St Bartholomew's to provide facilities for instructing nurses from the isolation hospitals of the Metropolitan Asylums Board.[76] As a pioneer of international cooperation she visited nursing schools in Paris, established a link between St Bartholomew's and the Salpêtrière Hospital, and in 1908 introduced a scheme for receiving French probationers for short periods of training at Bart's.[77]

In 1899 she founded the League of St Bartholomew's Nurses, on the model of the nursing alumnae associations which had been established in the United States during the previous decade. It was the first organisation of its kind in the United Kingdom, and all Bart's nurses who had gained their Hospital certificate were encouraged to join. Its stated purpose was to encourage high nursing standards among its members, to give them opportunities to meet socially and to provide financial support for those who had fallen on hard times; but there were undoubtedly further objectives, to give Bart's nurses a political platform and to promote among them the cause of registration. In its early years the League attracted much controversy. It became a vehicle for the views of Isla Stewart and of Mrs Bedford Fenwick, who frequently attended its meetings. Many of its members were active in the suffragette movement and Mrs Bedford Fenwick was herself an ardent supporter of women's suffrage. In 1905 the League also organised a course of lectures on bacteriology for trained nurses, at a time when the Hospital made no provision for postgraduate training.[78]

Isla Stewart was a woman of unusual talent. Her ability to inspire and motivate her nurses was combined with a remarkable personality. She had pride in her hospital and its nursing school, and she instilled this feeling in

Isla Stewart, Matron, with a group of Sisters. Undated photograph, c. 1905.

her staff and pupils, who responded by showing the depth of their love and respect for their Matron. By the end of her term of office Bart's-trained nurses were to be found working in almost every part of the world, and had taken with them their loyalty to their training school and its principles. Within the Hospital the Sisters and staff nurses unanimously supported their Matron in the fight for registration and professional standards. The Board of Governors also gave its tacit support by approving her programme of reforms; and in 1905 two trained nurses were elected as members of the Board, an event which would have been unthinkable a few years earlier.[79]

Stewart died in March 1910, while still in office as Matron. Her death brought anguish and dismay both to her friends and to the staff of the Hospital. The Sisters kept a two-day vigil in the mortuary chapel and then escorted her body in procession to Euston Station for burial in Scotland.[80] One of her former pupils, Rachael Cox Davies, Matron of the Royal Free Hospital, spoke for many when she said that Isla Stewart had built up a 'spirit of loyalty, of discipline, of honourable content and gladness in our work' which had left the nursing school 'united and happy as perhaps few others in the world have been'. She had 'filled her life with high ideals, and we, her nurses who loved her, tried to do the same . . . We were proud of ourselves, unspeakably proud of our fine old hospital, proud beyond words of our magnificent training; and the centre of it all was our Matron.'[81]

Chapter Four

MINISTERING ANGELS?
1910–1948

The appointment of a successor to Isla Stewart was made in the summer of 1910. The Governors did not select a Bart's-trained nurse; instead they chose Annie McIntosh, who was an Assistant Matron at the London Hospital. The announcement of their decision caused a great outcry. The new Matron had undergone only two years' training at the London and was therefore said to be ineligible even for a staff nurse's post at Bart's, for which three years' training was required. However the real, though unstated, cause of dissent was the perception that she was a protégée of Eva Luckes, the Matron of the London Hospital, who had emerged as the leading opponent of state registration and the arch-enemy of the professional organisation of nurses. The appointment ran counter to all that Isla Stewart had worked for, and her friends and supporters felt that their principles had been betrayed. Stewart had been in poor health for many months before her death and it was suspected that her opponents had been quietly planning a counter-offensive. The Board of Governors had perhaps been won over by Sir Henry Burdett, editor of the traditionalist journal *The Hospital*, who was a political ally of Eva Luckes. Mrs Bedford Fenwick responded to the appointment by forming a 'Defence of Nursing Standards Committee', which sent a petition to the Governors reminding them of the new Matron's unsatisfactory qualifications, but the Treasurer, Lord Sandhurst, refused to listen to the protests, saying that he would not be swayed by interference from outside the Hospital.[1]

The nurses at Bart's insisted that they felt no personal animosity against Annie McIntosh, but in her first years in office relations between the Matron and her staff were often difficult. In 1912 the Governors, at her request, imposed a ban on meetings in the Hospital on the subject of state registration.[2] As time passed, however, some of the ill-feeling disappeared, and McIntosh associated herself with the College of Nursing Ltd (later the Royal College of Nursing), which was founded in 1916 as a moderate body between the extreme views represented by Eva Luckes and Mrs Bedford Fenwick. The College accepted the case for registration but fought less stridently than the group led by Mrs Bedford Fenwick; it attracted the enmity of both Luckes and Fenwick but won over a number of Fenwick's supporters, including Rachael Cox Davies and Ellen Musson who had been Assistant Matron under Isla Stewart. When Annie McIntosh was co-opted onto the Council of the College of Nursing, Eva Luckes reluctantly had to accept that her reactionary opinions were no longer shared by her former pupil.[3] The League of St Bartholomew's Nurses remained faithful in its support of Mrs Bedford Fenwick, and in 1916 Rachael Cox Davies, who had succeeded Stewart as its president, offered to resign because her seat on the Council of the College appeared incompatible with League membership. She was persuaded to remain in office for a further twelve months, but when the post of president fell vacant in 1917 the members elected Helen Todd, who had long been a staunch supporter of the registrationists' cause. Todd claimed neutrality in the dispute between Fenwick and the College of Nursing, but under her presidency the League remained a platform for the views of the Fenwick group.[4]

One of the first measures taken by Annie McIntosh was the inauguration of midwifery training for nurses on Elizabeth Ward, which was converted to a lying-in ward in 1910. This was the Hospital's first maternity ward and as

Elizabeth Ward, c.1914, shortly after its conversion to a maternity ward.

Queen Alexandra visiting the Hospital in July 1917.

it had been established for the benefit of medical students the nurses had not expected to be able to train there. However the Matron and the obstetricians worked together to ensure that a small number of nurses who had gained their Hospital certificate could study for the newly established Central Midwives Board examination and attend the required number of cases in the ward. Elizabeth was not a large ward and only four to six nurses could be trained each year. Placements were eagerly sought after and a long waiting list soon grew up; many nurses had to seek their midwifery training outside St Bartholomew's. The use of Elizabeth Ward for obstetric nurse training was discontinued in 1923, to allow more places for medical students, and for forty years thereafter Bart's nurses had to obtain their midwifery experience elsewhere, generally at provincial or suburban hospitals.[5]

In the early years of the twentieth century 'special probationers' were still admitted to Bart's on payment of a fee, but McIntosh set out to reduce wherever possible the distinctions between them and the other probationers. In 1911 she extended the compulsory medical examination to candidates for special probationerships, on the ground that they needed to be just as fit as ordinary probationers. By 1918 there were few special probationers: their three-month training was no longer seen as having much practical value and most of those who applied for it did so because the Hospital was prepared to admit special probationers at a younger age than regular candidates. In July 1918 the minimum age for regular probationers was reduced to 21 and by the end of that year the admission of special probationers had ceased.[6]

During the First World War many Bart's-trained nurses went overseas and did excellent work in military hospitals; some even found themselves behind enemy lines and spent several weeks nursing wounded German troops. Others remained in London, nursing British and allied soldiers in the East Wing of St Bartholomew's or in the Territorial Force Nursing Service hospital at Camberwell, which was located in a former missionary college and was staffed partly by Bart's nurses and partly by women of the Voluntary Aid Detachments (VADs). The VADs were untrained and it seems that many of the trained nurses at Camberwell were determined to keep them in an inferior role, perhaps fearing that their contribution to the war effort might threaten the cause of state registration.[7] Some of the VADs were accepted at Bart's for training as probationers, but one former VAD in 1916 was advised by her Ward Sister to keep quiet about her past experiences, as VADs were perceived as 'stupid useless creatures' who were not wanted in the Hospital.[8]

By the end of the war the case for registration had won wide acceptance. It was finally granted in 1919, although the Government gave the nurses less autonomy than Mrs Bedford Fenwick and her supporters had hoped for. Christopher Addison, the Minister of Health who introduced the bill in Parliament, was a former lecturer in anatomy at the Medical School of St Bartholomew's Hospital, and Lord Sandhurst, Treasurer of the Hospital, steered the legislation through the House of Lords. Many Bart's-trained nurses were naturally among the first to apply for registration: the name of Mrs Bedford Fenwick appears on the register as state registered nurse no. 1 and Rachael Cox Davies as no. 3.[9]

The Nurses' Registration Act also set up the General Nursing Council for England and Wales to maintain the register and administer the state examination which for new entrants was to be the only means of admission to it. The establishment of the Council meant that for the first time a statutory body was monitoring the training of nurses and trying to impose a degree of uniformity on the standard of education in hospitals throughout the country. At Bart's, however, there was at first little sense of a loss of independence. Leading figures from the Hospital were prominent in the affairs of the Council: Sir Wilmot Herringham, a former Bart's Physician, was one of its first chairmen and in January 1926 when the chairmanship passed to a nurse the position was taken by Ellen Musson.[10] Moreover, the standard of training at St Bartholomew's was such that it had no difficulty in meeting the requirements of the Council in its early years. The state examination, introduced in 1923–5, was common to all hospitals, but Bart's like other leading hospitals also continued to set its own examinations and to award its certificate as a separate qualification.[11] Many of the old quarrels were allowed to subside and in 1921 as a gesture of goodwill the League of Nurses relaxed its rules so that a Matron or Assistant Matron could be an ex-officio member even if she did not hold the Hospital's certificate. Annie McIntosh never became a state registered nurse, but in 1925 she was elected president of the League and the *League News*, the members' journal, reported that her election was greeted with much rejoicing.[12]

By 1924 Bart's had a nursing staff of 323. There were 43 Sisters, of whom 28 were Ward Sisters and the others worked in the theatres, the out-patient and special departments, the Matron's office or the nurses' home. The three Night Superintendents, or Night Sisters, were junior in rank to the Ward and Departmental Sisters, although they took responsibility for all that happened in the ward blocks during the hours of darkness; these posts were generally filled by able nurses seeking promotion, who were waiting for a Ward Sister's post to fall vacant. Of the probationary and staff nurses, 138 worked in the wards on day duty and about 70 on night duty. A further 13 or 14 worked in theatres and 25 to 27 in the out-patient departments, most of the rest being 'floating' nurses who provided cover for sickness and holidays.[13] The pay of an uncertificated nurse, though still not generous, had substantially improved: before the First World War a probationer in her first year received an annual salary of £8, but this was increased to £14 in 1917 and to £20 in 1921.[14]

In Annie McIntosh's early years as Matron St Bartholomew's did not have a Preliminary Training School of the sort which existed at the London, Guy's and St Thomas' Hospitals. A new probationer on her first day at Bart's would be shown to her shared bedroom in the nurses' home and given a tour of the Hospital before supper. The next morning she reported to the Matron's office and was then sent to her allotted ward, where the Sister or staff nurse would immediately put her to work.[15] The absence of preliminary training created problems both for the senior nursing staff and for the probationers themselves. In McIntosh's opinion newly arrived probationers were 'practically useless for the first month or two, and . . . a burden on the Sisters and staff nurses'. One nurse recalled that new probationers often 'had to guess at what was required by the staff nurse, who directed them to fetch articles they had never heard of'. Many newcomers were confused and distressed by their first days on the wards. In later life one

The Preliminary Training School in King Square, Finsbury, 1933.

who arrived as a probationer in the 1920s remembered that she was wholly ignorant of hospital life, had never made beds or taken temperatures, and was taken aback on being addressed as 'nurse' within a few hours of entering the Hospital. Her first impression on setting foot in a surgical ward was of noise, activity and an overpowering smell of chloroform, which made her feel sickened and terrified.[16]

The need for preliminary training had been recognised by Isla Stewart as early as 1906 but had been deferred by the Governors because of lack of accommodation. Annie McIntosh renewed the call for a Preliminary Training School in 1911 and the Governors considered the matter again in 1919, but still nothing was done.[17] The Preliminary Training School finally opened in 1925 in the former special probationers' home in King Square, where four classrooms had been erected in the garden. Pupils were trained there for six weeks, with an examination in the seventh week before they were admitted to work on the wards. They paid six guineas for the preliminary course, which at that time was equivalent to almost four months' salary for a first-year probationer. At King Square they were taught elementary anatomy, physiology, hygiene, sick cookery and bandaging. The latter was an important part of a nurse's early training as no other fixative was then available and dressings were always secured with bandages. Some of the techniques taught on the course were already practically obsolete, and the pupils made linseed poultices on teased tow, a skill which they would never have to use in the wards; but other teaching methods were more advanced, by the standards of that time, and one of the classrooms was equipped with a model bed and ward equipment so that an element of simulated practical nursing could be included.[18]

Once accepted into the Hospital, the probationer of the 1920s settled into a daily routine. Her working day, though less onerous than that of her late Victorian predecessors, was still very long. When on day duty she would be woken early in the morning by the noise of the meat wagons going over the cobbles in Little Britain on their way to Smithfield Market. Breakfast was at 6.30 a.m., and she started work at 7 a.m. with washing to be done and beds to be made to put the ward in order for the day. After a short break and a change to a clean apron, she was back in the ward at 10 a.m. The rest of the morning might be spent cleaning, polishing, sterilising instruments, taking temperatures, doing fomentations or preparing dressings. She was allowed thirty minutes for her midday meal which was eaten in the nurses' dining room. Nurses were not permitted to leave the dining room until the end of the half-hour, so most took knitting or reading matter to occupy them until it was time to return to the ward.[19]

Nurses in the dining room, c. 1929.

In the early afternoon, if it were a so-called 'Full Day', came the formal ceremony of the Physician's or Surgeon's ward round, when the great man would proceed from bed to bed accompanied by the Ward Sister and staff nurse and followed by his retinue of medical students. This was the great moment of the day, for which the nurses worked hard to make the ward look its best. Trays were laid with the articles which might be needed. All the patients were confined to bed, with their bedding carefully adjusted and the position of the beds measured to ensure that they were in a straight line parallel to the wall. In one ward a custom of pre-war years was still observed and the junior probationer was required to stand in attendance on the procession, carrying the doctor's quill pen and inkpot. In every ward clean aprons were put on and the probationers stopped whatever they were doing, as silence was enforced during the round and no other activity permitted.[19]

All probationers, especially in their first year, had a large number of domestic duties every day. Theatre nurses prepared all the dressings for operations and packed them into drums for sterilisation. In the wards, scrubbing and polishing the floors was the task of the 'floor woman' (the successor to the Victorian 'scrubber') and there was a ward maid who lit the fires, did the washing up and acted as personal maid to the Ward Sister. All the rest of the cleaning – beds, cupboards and bathrooms in the wards, taps, operating tables and other furniture in the theatres – was done by the probationers. In the years immediately after the First World War probationers were also expected to clean walls and windows in the wards. Sisters insisted on their wards being kept spotless. Much of the cleaning was done in the afternoons, on days when there was no ward round.[20] Between 3 and 4 p.m. the nurses prepared and served the patients' tea and then, if time allowed, had their own tea in the ward kitchen. After tea the patients were washed and put to bed. Later the patients had to be given their supper, and finally the ward had to be swept and cleared up. The probationers had two or three hours off duty during the day, and finished work at 8 p.m. At that hour a bell was rung in the ward to call for silence, and Sister said prayers as the day shift ended. Once again the nurses put on a clean apron and went one by one into Sister's room to wish her good-night; their supper followed immediately.[21]

In every ward of the Hospital this routine was repeated daily throughout the 1920s, and continued with only minor changes during the 1930s. Lectures by the medical staff were given once a week, just as they had been forty or fifty years earlier, and for probationers on day duty they were held after supper, from 8.30 to 9.30 p.m. Nurses who were trained during that era later recalled that the lectures were generally excellent, and that they had felt privileged to be taught by some of the leading figures of the medical

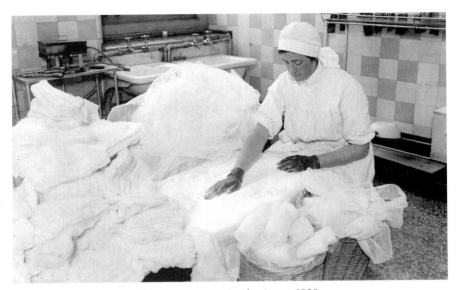

Theatre nurse preparing dressings, c.1929.

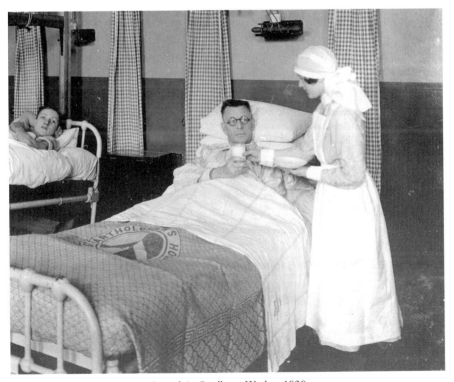

At work in Sandhurst Ward, c.1929.

world; but no matter how good the lecture, at the end of a long day's work some probationers inevitably fell asleep before it was finished. If there was no lecture the nurses could sit in their communal sitting room before a coal fire, or go to their rooms to study or for tea and gossip. Each nurse had to be in her own room by 10 p.m. and lights were turned out by 10.30.[22]

By the standards of a later era, the experience gained by probationers in the 1920s was limited, as they had little formal tuition apart from the lectures and would normally expect to spend three months on duty in the same ward. All nurses changed wards four times a year, and at Sunday breakfast on the changeover day the new allocations were read out and each probationer learnt where she would be working for the next three months. If she was assigned to night duty, this would also be for a three-month period, during which she would attend lectures in the early morning. Although day nurses ate in the dining room, night staff still took their meals on the wards, and the junior night probationer on each ward would be expected to prepare a meal for her senior in the ward kitchen at midnight. She would also polish the brasses, bedpans and pewter bowls; the senior would do light mending of the ward linen and cook breakfast for all the patients.[23]

A probationer was required to attend 28 lectures during her first year, followed by a practical course of instruction in bandaging. Second-year probationers had 32 lectures, one a week from October to May, and third-years attended 22 lectures. The lecture syllabus had altered little since Isla Stewart revised it in 1906. The Matron's first-year lectures dealt with such matters as ethics, principles of asepsis, bedmaking, washing, feeding, hot and cold treatments, temperatures, pulses and hypodermic injections, as well as some survivals from an earlier age such as cupping and the application of leeches. A young doctor gave lectures to the first-year probationers on anatomy and physiology. One of the Assistant Physicians taught the second-years about fevers, diseases of the internal organs and the use of drugs, while an Assistant Surgeon lectured to them on surgical nursing, which included the treatment of wounds, orthopaedic nursing and the nursing of post-operative patients. Specialist aspects of nursing were dealt with in the third year, with nine lectures on bacteriology, five on gynaecological nursing and three on ophthalmic nursing. A series of five third-year classes on theatre nursing and sterilisation, and a fourth-year course on hygiene and public health, were the only significant additions that had been made to the lecture syllabus since 1906. The Matron was always present at lectures given by the medical staff, and personally attended all the nursing examinations.[24]

By 1925, according to the annual report issued by the Treasurer of the Hospital, 'it was felt that nurses in training required some additional help in the way of systematic instruction, to enable them to derive the fullest advantage from the various lectures'. Many other hospitals were already employing Sister Tutors – senior nurses who were qualified to teach probationers and had no immediate responsibilities for patient care – and in August 1925 Annie McIntosh appointed Margaret Hitch as the first Sister Tutor at Bart's. In this capacity she delivered all the nursing lectures which had previously been given by the Matron, although the bulk of the lecturing was still undertaken by the medical staff. Probationers valued the help which she was able to give, though she could only teach them in the evenings or in their off-duty time. They were expected to write notes of the lectures which they attended, and the Sister Tutor checked what they had written and offered correction or further explanation where she felt it was needed. Margaret Hitch was a forward-looking teacher who saw the need for an improved theoretical basis to nurse training. She wrote a number of books and articles on nursing, including a paper for the *League News* in 1932 in which she advocated an extended preliminary course that could be run independently of hospital authorities.[25]

The life of a nurse in the 1920s and 1930s was circumscribed by rules and regulations. Probationers never spoke to a senior member of the medical staff, and were forbidden to converse with medical students while on duty. Every new entrant was firmly told that a nurse should always walk, and never run, except in cases of haemorrhage or fire. Many of the other rules, which were strictly enforced at the time, now seem very petty. Patients' tea had to be served on trays, and a nurse who came out of the ward kitchen with a cup in her hand would be sent back to put it on a tray. First-year probationers were not allowed to sit in the Square, and those in their second year and above could do so only on summer evenings. Until 1931 nurses were not allowed out of the Hospital in the evening without a special pass. They could not have visitors in their rooms without permission and were strictly forbidden to enter the quarters of the resident medical staff, although they could receive male visitors in the nurses' general sitting rooms.[26]

Like other hospitals at that time, St Bartholomew's also had meticulous rules about the wearing of uniform. Nurses were not allowed to enter a ward out of uniform, and even in the dining room an apology to the Sister in charge was expected from any nurse not correctly attired.[27] Aprons had to be starched and ironed, one inch shorter than the dress, with seven pleats on each side. Belts were to be two inches wide, and collars one and three-quarter inches. Sleeves had to be long, with an opening extending not less than six inches from the wrist, and fastened with exactly six buttons. At the wrist was a detachable cuff, two and a half inches wide. There were strict rituals about sleeves and cuffs. In 1914 cuffs had been worn only when a ward round was in progress or when Matron was visiting the ward, but by

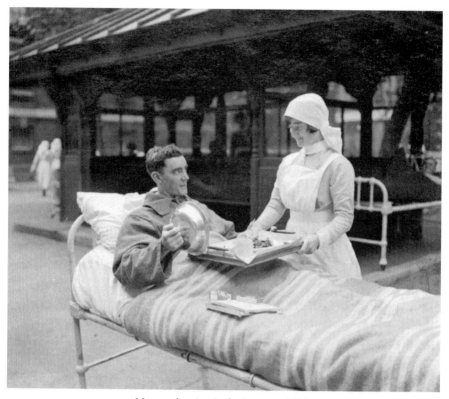

Nurse and patient in the Square, c.1929.

the late 1920s sleeves were buttoned and cuffs worn for serving food or drink, for officially speaking to Sister or for leaving the ward. When working in the ward at other times the nurse was expected to roll her sleeves and place her cuffs in her pocket. However if she gave even a glass of water to a patient with her sleeves rolled up she could expect a reprimand from Sister. Further rules dictated the length of her skirt: in 1924 it had to be six inches off the ground, though the rule was progressively altered to eight, nine and (in the early 1930s) ten inches. The Sister in charge of the nurses' home insisted that all items of uniform should be exactly correct, and would send back to her room a nurse whose shoes were not shining or whose dress fell short of the highest standards. She also demanded that hair should be almost completely hidden under a nurse's cap.[28] In 1926–7 the frilled cap with strings tied under the chin, which had been worn since late Victorian times, was replaced by a cap made from a square lawn handkerchief, without strings. A new square cap for Sisters was introduced at about the same time, although those who wished were allowed to retain the older style.[29]

In the 1920s Sisters still lived on the wards and ate some of their meals there. They each had a bedroom and sitting room next to the ward, and in these rooms, which they filled with their personal belongings,[30] they slept and spent much of their off-duty time. No separate bathrooms were provided. When she wanted a bath, a Sister could walk across the Square to

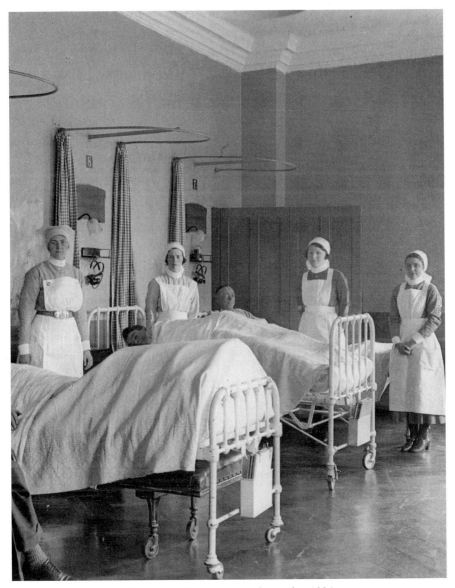

Sister Smithfield with nurses in her ward, c.1934.

the nurses' home or use the patients' bath in the sluice room at the end of the ward. Even in the 1930s many older Sisters were reluctant to depart from tradition and chose the latter. When a probationer came on night duty her first task was to clean and disinfect the bath, put out a chair and bathmat for Sister's use, run the bath water and perhaps bring a vase of flowers into the room. The wards were still arranged in dormitory style, so the lights were dimmed while Sister in her dressing-gown walked the length of the ward to reach the bath. One of the probationers would mount guard at the door, to ensure that the houseman's night round did not start until Sister was safely back in her room. If Sister wanted a bedtime drink after her bath, a probationer would make it and carry it to her room. In the morning she would be woken by the senior night probationer who would bring her a cup of tea and give her a report as she lay in bed.[31]

A Ward Sister's post had by then acquired considerable prestige and many Sisters were very conscious of their status. They did not as a rule mix socially with staff nurses or others below them in the hierarchy. Sisters of long standing often looked with condescension on those who had only recently 'gone into blue'. In the wards they ruled with an iron hand. Their 'charge' required them to maintain discipline, strict economy and courteous behaviour on the part of their staff, and to report any misconduct to the Matron. A young nurse was expected to obey Sister's word without question, and only the most rebellious probationer would think of flouting it. Some Sisters made a conscientious effort to encourage and instruct the probationers assigned to them but in many wards no instruction was offered and the probationers learnt only by observation. They were not taught, or expected to ask, the reason for any procedure or technique being used, and even in the best wards had to be content simply to learn the routines which were required. New arrivals soon discovered that the best way of avoiding trouble was to learn to do things in the way Sister liked. To a young nurse at the start of her training some Sisters seemed autocratic; others preferred to ignore new probationers altogether. In the wards with the worst reputation probationers were criticised openly in front of patients, found themselves blamed whenever a patient's condition deteriorated, or were constantly told that they lacked any of the personal and professional attributes which would enable them to qualify as a nurse. Little attempt was made by the Hospital authorities to restrain Sisters who chose to behave in this way.[32]

Despite these tribulations the probationers do not seem to have been unhappy or resentful of the discipline and long hours. Though often tired and footsore after a day's work, they saw their training as a kind of endurance test, in which their survival proved their value as nurses. Many who were trained at this time have recalled that the shared experience of adversity gave a sense of comradeship which enabled them to persevere. Indeed most felt a genuine pride in the Hospital and in their work. Many had mothers who had trained there as nurses, or fathers or brothers who had been medical students. Although entrants to Bart's were no longer presented with Isla Stewart's vision of professional nursing, Annie McIntosh followed her predecessor in encouraging a spirit of loyalty to the Hospital. At a time when St Bartholomew's promoted itself as 'the Mother Hospital of the British Empire' it was natural for the nurses to believe that theirs was the finest hospital in the world. Inevitably their sense of belonging to a uniquely excellent institution discouraged them from taking a wider view of the nursing profession, and made them receptive to the idea that that their own needs and wishes should take second place to the interests of the Hospital. Many years later a former probationer wrote of the 1920s and 1930s that she and her contemporaries were offered 'the role-image of the Bart's nurse . . . a ministering angel prepared to support fatigue and toil for the privilege of serving the sick . . . never hasty or sharp spoken, and indifferent to low pay'; within the Hospital 'intelligence was less esteemed than conformity to the role'.[33] These attitudes were more reminiscent of Florence Nightingale than of Isla Stewart or Mrs Bedford Fenwick, and to the end of her term of office Annie McIntosh remained unsympathetic to Fenwick and to the ideas which she represented.[34]

An image of a Bart's nurse, used to raise funds for the Hospital in the second quarter of the twentieth century.

By the time of Annie McIntosh's retirement in March 1927, the nursing staff had all but forgotten how unpopular her appointment had been. Sisters and nurses thronged to wish her farewell as she left the Matron's house and drove out through the Henry VIII Gate for the last time.[35] In her successor Helen Dey the Hospital at last had a Matron who was a Bart's-trained nurse. Born in 1888, Helen Dey had come to St Bartholomew's in November 1909 and had spent her first five months of training under Isla Stewart. However the larger part of her education had been under Annie McIntosh, and as Matron her approach owed something to each of her predecessors. Her students were taught that the Bart's ideal was of nursing as a vocation, to which the professional element was at most a supplement. In choosing candidates for training, Dey sought women who were articulate and reasonably well educated, but laid more stress on the need for them to be gentle, sympathetic, industrious and willing to show constant thought for others. Most of those whom she selected were from middle-class but not academic backgrounds, for she held that 'university women' would not do well as nurses. Probationers were encouraged to believe that to be 'a good Bart's nurse' was more important than passing the final state examination, and that the Hospital certificate was far more to be coveted than the title of state registered nurse.[36] On the other hand Dey also believed that experienced nurses should move in circles outside their own hospital, and should strive to obtain better pay and conditions for the profession as a whole. She became known as a campaigner on the General Nursing Council and elsewhere, not least in her efforts to raise standards in 'lesser' training schools to the level of excellence which she maintained at Bart's.[37]

In contrast to Annie McIntosh, who wrote her business letters in longhand, Helen Dey had all her letters typed and kept a copy of each one. Dealing with correspondence was an important part of the Matron's work, and Dey replied personally to almost every letter on nursing matters, including the hundreds of enquiries about training which were received every year.[38] Elsie Hall, later Sister Harmsworth, worked as Night Sister in the 1930s and has recalled how Dey was always busy with correspondence when she went into the Matron's office in the early morning to give a report on the events of the previous night. Dey often seemed to be engrossed in reading her letters but was an acute listener; deficiencies in the Night Sister's report were invariably questioned.[39]

Helen Dey was an imposing and awe-inspiring figure and most of her staff were more than a little afraid of her. However she took a genuine interest in their welfare and was always willing to support them in times of difficulty, or to use her influence to advance the careers of those who were suitably qualified. She was a committed Anglican and although church attendance on

*Helen Dey, Matron 1927–49, with Lord Stanmore, Treasurer, in Bowlby Ward on the Hospital's
annual View Day, c.1937.*

the part of nurses was no longer compulsory she actively encouraged it. Sunday evensong in the church of St Bartholomew the Less was arranged so that nurses could attend after their supper and the church was generally full every week.[40]

As Matron Helen Dey particularly wanted to see trained nurses better paid, in order to encourage them to remain in the profession and seek promotion. Under her influence St Bartholomew's Hospital followed the policy of the (Royal) College of Nursing in widening differentials between trained nurses and probationers, and in 1928–9 the salaries of Sisters and senior staff nurses were increased by more than twenty per cent. A Sister then earnt between £95 and £110 per annum, and from 1928 all her meals, as well as her lodging, were provided by the Hospital free of charge. The Sisters had been given a separate dining room from the probationers and other nurses, and the meals served there were generally thought to be of better quality. Dey told the League of Nurses that salaries for trained staff were higher at St Bartholomew's than at any other voluntary hospital in the British Isles.[41] At the same time Bart's discontinued its own pension arrangements and made it obligatory for newly appointed or promoted staff to join the Federated Superannuation Scheme for Nurses and Hospital Officers.[42] This was the first occasion on which the Hospital made use of a nationally agreed scheme in setting conditions of service for its nursing staff.

Until the 1920s St Bartholomew's suffered from a shortage of accommodation both for teaching purposes and for housing the growing numbers of nurses. The original nurses' home in Little Britain had rapidly become too small, and as late as 1890 some nurses had still been obliged to sleep in cubicles near a diphtheria ward in the South Wing.[43] Temporary accommodation had been provided in the late nineteenth century in other buildings in Little Britain and Smithfield, and for a short time in the Clerk's house in the North Wing. In 1902 Bart's obtained a large four-storey building, at the rear of the South Wing, which had previously belonged to Christ's Hospital and was suitable for conversion to nurses' accommodation.[44] However other leading hospitals had purpose-built nurses' homes and Bart's naturally wished to provide the same standard of housing. Funds for a new nurses' home were raised before the First World War but building work did not start until 1921. Queen Mary's Nurses' Home was brought into use in three stages between 1923 and 1930. Its residents enjoyed improved washing facilities, and single bedrooms in contrast to the double rooms in the old homes. The former Christ's Hospital building was demolished in 1927–8 and a Surgical Block (now part of the King George V Block) was built on the site and opened in 1930. In the wards of the new block the Sisters were provided with sitting rooms, which

Relaxing in Queen Mary's Nurses' Home, 1930s.

were reserved for their personal use when off-duty as well as in working hours, but their bedrooms were in the nurses' home.[45]

Two rooms in the basement of Queen Mary's Nurses' Home were equipped as a study room and classroom. These were the Hospital's first purpose-built facilities for nurse education, and their opening in April 1929 meant that nursing lectures no longer had to be given in the lecture theatres of the Medical School. Three months later the Isla Stewart Memorial

Library was opened on the site of the former Matron's house and was stocked with reference books for nursing studies. Until the 1920s the Hospital had not used any particular name to describe its nursing school, but in anticipation of the school acquiring its own premises it was given a title: the St Bartholomew's Hospital Training School for Nurses. The new name was used on the front of the training prospectus which was produced for the first time in 1928.[46]

In the early 1930s it was noted that the number of nurses reporting sick had fallen sharply during the previous decade, and the medical staff attributed this to the improved accommodation in Queen Mary's Home, as well as reduced working hours and a better diet. Nevertheless in February 1929 an influenza epidemic brought 73 nurses off work, and half of a ward had to be emptied of patients and given over to sick nurses. One of the commonest causes for nurses reporting sick was a septic finger. Dressings at that time were still done with swabs held in the fingers, pricks from safety-pins were common and there were no antibiotics. Winifred Hector, later to be Principal Tutor at the Training School, has recalled that in the mid 1930s 'if you opened the door of the dressing room in the nurses' sickrooms, you were met by a cloud of steam [and] half-a-dozen nurses would be sitting soaking septic fingers'. She also remembered an evening in 1937 when she and a few other nurses were doing a crossword puzzle in a room in Queen Mary's Home: 'someone asked if we had heard of a drug called prontosil which would cure infections; we said no, and returned to the crossword, unaware that a major revolution in our work was taking place'. In the following year the Hospital obtained a supply of 'M & B 693', an early sulphonamide produced by the firm of May and Baker, and the treatment of septic conditions at last became possible.[47]

Under Annie McIntosh the number of nursing staff had grown only a little, but during Helen Dey's term of office it increased substantially. When she became Matron in 1927 she inherited a total staff of 326, but by 1934 this figure had grown to 406, and by the outbreak of war in 1939 to 512. Each general medical or surgical ward then had a day staff of eight (one Sister, two fourth-year nurses who had passed the state examination but were awaiting their Hospital certificate, three probationers in their second or third year and two in their first year). Of the two staff on night duty in the ward, one would be in her third year and one in her first or second.[48] Only a few specialist wards had a certificated staff nurse, though a number of certificated nurses worked in the operating theatres and out-patient departments. Senior staff nurses in the theatres, and any others who were 'acting up' as temporary Sisters, wore a distinctive pink uniform. They were then formally called 'appointed staff nurses' or 'charge nurses in pink', but came to be known simply as 'pinks'.[49]

The new sulphonamide tablets, c.1938.

The increase in staff numbers enabled the working week to be further reduced and more time off given. Until 1931 nurses had one whole day and one half day off per fortnight but in that year it became possible for every nurse to be guaranteed a whole day off each week. The hours of duty were 56 per week in 1931, but by the end of the decade this figure had been reduced to 52.[50] Helen Dey constantly sought opportunities to enhance the living conditions of her nurses, and in 1937 she succeeded in persuading the Zachary Merton Trust to endow a convalescent home for Bart's nurses at Northwood in Middlesex. The Zachary Merton Home was open, not only to nurses who needed to recuperate after illness, but also to those wishing to relax there on their days off. To nurses whose families lived far from London it offered a welcome retreat. It was unfortunate that the Home had to be closed at the start of the Second World War in 1939, and though Dey fought to have it reopened after the war she was never able to achieve this.[51]

The number of teaching staff also grew while Helen Dey was Matron. A second Sister Tutor was appointed in 1929, and by 1939 Margaret Hitch was Senior Tutor with two Sister Tutors under her; there were also three teaching staff in the Preliminary Training School.[52] By the 1930s the Sister Tutors were giving regular weekly revision and coaching classes to all nurses in training; each nurse was expected to attend these in addition to the weekly lecture. In 1933 Dey arranged additional lectures in dietetics and diseases of children for second-year nurses and in dermatology and diseases of the ear, nose and throat for third-years. She also moved the time of the lectures to 6.15 pm so that, for nurses on day duty, they took place during rather than after normal working hours.[53]

When the Second World War broke out in 1939 the centre of London was expected to be an immediate target for aerial attack. The Preliminary Training School was moved from King Square to the site in Northwood where the Zachary Merton Home had been established two years earlier. Many of the wards at St Bartholomew's were promptly shut, including those in the East Wing and Casualty (later Lucas) Block. These were the last wards which still had Sisters' bedrooms attached and with their closure the long tradition of Sisters living on their wards came to an end. Most of the nursing staff and patients were evacuated from central London. In the first two weeks of September 308 Bart's nurses were moved to Hill End Hospital at St Albans. A further 52 went to Cell Barnes Hospital in the same locality and only 133 remained at Smithfield.[54]

Hill End was a psychiatric hospital and conditions there were very poor. The buildings were infested with mice and cockroaches, and bats flew in the corridors. The nurses had almost no privacy, sleeping five or six to a room or in a large open ward with very little furniture. Hill End had no operating

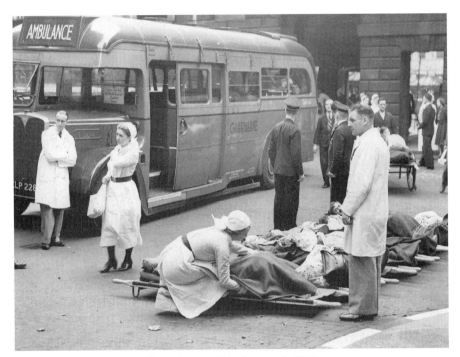

Evacuation to Hill End Hospital, 1939.

theatres or laboratory services and in the early months of the war these had
to be established as a matter of urgency. When the first Bart's nurses arrived
there was no gas and scarcely any equipment in the wards, and they had to
sterilise instruments, test specimens and cook food using primus stoves.
Working conditions were slowly improved but throughout the war the staff
had to nurse far more beds than was usual in peacetime. In 1938
St Bartholomew's had 763 beds but in 1940 there were more than 1100 at
Hill End alone, with over sixty beds in each ward. The total number of beds
divided between the three sites was more than 1600, although the nursing
staff was no larger than in the immediate pre-war years. Inevitably all moves
towards a shorter working week had to be curtailed and the nurses again
found themselves working very long hours. Particular crises occurred when
there was a heavy intake of military patients: in the aftermath of the
evacuation of Dunkirk, six hundred untreated casualties arrived at Hill End
in a single week.[55]

A few wards on the Smithfield site remained open throughout the war,
primarily to receive air-raid casualties and other emergency cases. As a
precaution against bombing raids, only the lower floors of the Medical and

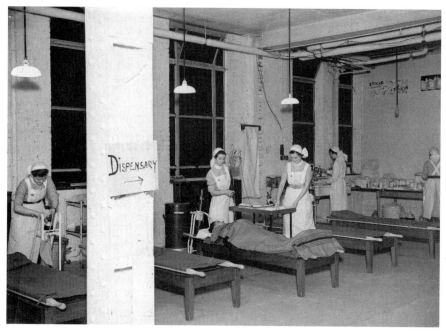

Nurses working in wartime casualty clearing station, 1939.

Surgical Blocks were in use, and patients were moved out to Hill End as soon as practicable. If casualties were high, patients would be transported to Hill End within 24 hours or less, to make room for the next arrivals. When the Hospital's electricity supply was cut off during the worst of the raids on London, the nurses removed the black-out curtains from the windows and carried on their work by the light of the burning city.[56]

Salaries for nurses in training had remained unchanged at St Bartholomew's since the early 1920s and by the start of the Second World War had fallen behind the rates of pay at local authority hospitals. The standard of training at Bart's, and the high regard in which its certificate was held, meant that despite the low pay the Hospital had little difficulty in attracting recruits, even at a time of a national shortage of candidates for nursing. However by the end of the 1930s it was felt that there were 'not nearly enough of the best type of candidates' and in August 1941, when wartime pressures made it imperative to maintain the number of recruits, salaries were increased to £30 for first-year nurses, £35 for second-years and £40 for third-years.[57]

Teaching and examinations were transferred to Hill End at the start of the war. The grey first-year uniform was discontinued in 1942 because of a textile shortage, and new entrants wore striped dresses like their seniors. Wartime economy measures also led to the disappearance of apron straps, and short-sleeved dresses with soft collars were introduced for nurses in training.[58] Margaret Hitch left Bart's in 1942 and for the remaining years of the war the Training School in its Hertfordshire exile was run by Gwendolen Fellows. She was remembered as one who 'always had an image of the true Bart's nurse – hardworking, punctual, unfailingly kind, skilled, neat and well-informed', a picture which she constantly put before her students.[59]

Her successor, Winifred Hector, was appointed to have charge of the School in 1946. Born in the west of England, she came from a working-class family: her father was an engine-driver on the Great Western Railway. Before entering nursing she had begun a university course but had been obliged to withdraw on medical advice. As a young nurse at Bart's in the 1930s she had found that her background was very different to that of most of her contemporaries and she was encouraged by Helen Dey to take up teaching. During her 24 years as Principal Tutor, Winifred Hector acquired a considerable reputation as an educationalist. She believed that being 'a good Bart's nurse' was not incompatible with passing the state examination, and upheld both aims to those whom she taught. At the same time she insisted that there was more to a nurse's education than merely assisting doctors and learning techniques by rote in order to pass a practical examination. She wanted to show that nursing was a career for women who could think for themselves, and that their training could be used to help them relate effectively to the needs of patients as well as the requirements of the medical staff.[60]

In June 1946, thirteen months after the end of the war in Europe and about two years before the inauguration of the National Health Service, a frail elderly patient was admitted to Lawrence Ward in the Surgical Block. At the age of 89 Mrs Bedford Fenwick had fallen and fractured her femur, and had been taken to the Hospital from which she had resigned as Matron almost sixty years before. She was discharged in November and died at a friend's house in the early months of 1947. Her admission to St Bartholomew's caused a certain stir of interest among some of the nursing staff, but to others her name meant little. She had gradually distanced herself from the Hospital and though she remained a member of the League of Nurses she had become less active in its affairs. After her death her achievements were largely forgotten for a quarter of a century and interest did not revive until Winifred Hector published her biography in 1973. She remained uncommemorated at Bart's until 1989 when it was decided to name a ward in her honour.[61]

Chapter Five

THE NATIONAL HEALTH SERVICE: 1948–1974

Although Bart's had been a wealthy hospital in the Victorian age, its resources in the twentieth century were barely enough to keep pace with ever-increasing costs. The Governors found themselves obliged to seek new sources of funding in order to pay their staff and meet the other expenses of the Hospital. In 1943 the salaries of most nurses at St Bartholomew's were assimilated to a national scale when the Governors decided to adopt the pay recommendations of the Rushcliffe Committee. Acceptance of the Rushcliffe scale was optional but the Ministry of Health offered the inducement of a grant to meet part of the cost, and at a time of growing financial difficulties the Hospital was not in a position to reject a subsidy.[1] By the end of the Second World War most of the staff were aware that a reorganisation of the nation's hospitals would soon be necessary, and it was gradually accepted that in future Bart's would be largely financed by the state. When the post-war government set up the National Health Service the Board of Governors reluctantly acquiesced in the transfer of the Hospital to state control, and Bart's was acquired by the Ministry of Health in July 1948.

In the years which followed the Ministry attempted, with varying degrees of success, to impose nationally agreed standards and conditions of work for nurses and other staff. The Hospital's freedom to determine its own policies in nurse education was also being eroded by the powers granted to the General Nursing Council and after 1949 to the Area Nurse Training Committee. Nevertheless it was still managed by a Board of Governors which had been able to retain a considerable degree of autonomy, and the Governors tried to preserve the distinctiveness of Bart's wherever they could. The nursing staff remained a closed and largely self-sufficient community, whose members were trained within the Hospital and lived, ate and slept there. As in Victorian times the social highlight of the year continued to be the annual View Day in May, when the Sisters paid their early-morning visit to Covent Garden market to buy flowers for their wards; in the afternoon they offered a splendid tea to visitors, and the Governors went in formal procession to inspect the Hospital. Newly appointed Sisters in the 1950s still had their 'charge' read to them by the Treasurer in a formal ceremony in the

Sisters in procession, 1948.

North Wing, just as their predecessors had for centuries past. Like many hospitals, St Bartholomew's also sought to preserve the familiar uniforms of its nursing staff, and the seniority of a Bart's nurse could still be recognised from the colour of her belt. Sisters continued to wear their blue uniforms and distinctive square caps, and the Matron wore a conspicuously fine white headcovering with her plain black dress. The Ministry of Health did not recognise the grade of 'staff nurse in pink' but Bart's retained the pink uniform and for some years the Governors continued to pay an enhanced rate to those entitled to wear it.[2]

Within the Hospital the traditional view of nursing as a secondary profession to medicine was widely held, and there may still have been doctors who found it hard to accept that nursing required knowledge as well as devotion and kindliness. In the early 1950s Winifred Hector, concerned lest her medical colleagues should fail to understand the need for skilled and intelligent nurses, felt it necessary to argue the case for nurse education in the pages of the *St Bartholomew's Hospital Journal*. Her reasoning, however, owed as much to Annie McIntosh and Helen Dey as to the pioneers of nurse training at Bart's. While dismissing the idea that a good nurse 'needs a kind heart only', she stated her belief that nurses were 'practical people' and that the value of nursing theory was proved only by the quality of a nurse's work in the wards. In her view the Bart's ideal was of nursing as a vocation, and she insisted that training was designed to enhance the nurse's practical value at the patient's bedside.[3]

Although the Hospital's recruitment literature had begun to refer to 'student nurses' instead of 'probationers',[4] the new terminology had not been matched by any significant change in the students' role. Like their contemporaries in other training schools they were students in name only, and teaching took second place to ward duties. The long-standing ceremony of 'election of probationers' remained unaltered and continued to be so called until 1956. The students were widely known as 'pros', both by their seniors and among themselves. While some schools had given up the practice of holding their own examinations, students at St Bartholomew's continued to sit the Hospital's examination and if successful were awarded its certificate after four years, in addition to their state registration. Bart's generally ensured that its own examinations were more difficult than their state counterparts, in order to maintain the prestige of the certificate.

Helen Dey retired in the summer of 1949 and was succeeded as Matron by Joan Loveridge. Like her predecessor, Loveridge was a Bart's-trained nurse, and devoted to the Hospital and its traditions, but in contrast to Dey's aloofness of manner she was approachable and relaxed. On taking up her post the new Matron realised that the facilities at St Bartholomew's were in some respects unsatisfactory. The Training School was divided between Smithfield and Hill End and there were difficulties in providing regular courses of lectures and classes when the nurses were working at such widely separated sites. All lectures were given in the evening at the end of the working day; night nurses rose early in order to attend. The ratio of 1.6 beds per nurse at Bart's compared badly with the statistics at many other leading hospitals in the late 1940s: the London Hospital had 1.4 beds for every nurse while the Middlesex had almost achieved a parity of one nurse for every bed.[5] Nevertheless because of its reputation St Bartholomew's was able to attract the cream of applicants for nurse training, with ten candidates for every place. Its status as a teaching hospital linked to a Medical College meant that practically every type of case could be seen and student nurses had the benefit of tuition from highly experienced medical staff. The practical training in the wards, however inadequate by the standards of a later era, was far superior to that offered at most smaller hospitals, and visitors came regularly from all parts of the world to see the School.

Although the Matron no longer gave lectures to student nurses the School and its staff were still very much under her control and she interviewed all candidates for training. When Joan Loveridge became Matron she immediately proposed to introduce the block system of teaching, already used in many large hospitals in Britain and overseas, which gave student nurses occasional 'blocks' of several weeks of concentrated study away from the wards. She first hoped to set up a block scheme in April 1950 but found it impossible to take nurses away from the wards for the necessary length of time.[6] In seeking a compromise she established a system of regular study days for nurses in training. Student nurses then began their education with 10½ weeks at the Preliminary Training School, which had moved in 1948 from Northwood to Piggott's Manor at Letchmore Heath, Hertfordshire. Their tuition in these first weeks covered the syllabus for part I of the preliminary state examination. On entry to the Hospital they were given six weekly lectures on nursing theory. After 1950 these were the only lectures which students had to attend at the close of a day's work in the wards, and during the rest of their training they were allowed 42 separate days of classroom study.[7]

A month before part II of the preliminary state examination at the end of her first year a nurse attended four study days on successive Mondays, with lectures on nursing, theatre technique and psychology. In the course of her second year she had fourteen study days when she learnt about medicine, surgery, diseases of children, dermatology, materia medica and dietetics. Her third-year study days covered gynaecology, bacteriology, venereal disease, ophthalmology and diseases of the ear, nose and throat, besides further aspects of medicine and nursing. The tuition, with much of its basis in

Piggott's Manor, Letchmore Heath, site of the Preliminary Training School from 1948 to 1971.

simplified medical science, was intended to mould her into a competent hospital nurse; as yet training schools offered no instruction in community nursing. In other respects, however, the introduction of study days marked a considerable educational advance. Films and lantern slides were used for teaching as well as pathological specimens and the traditional lectures and demonstrations. Departmental visits and ward rounds for nurses began to be arranged, with the first round conducted by one of the Surgeons in Harmsworth Ward in September 1950. Finally ten revision study days, with further lectures on theatre technique, report writing and ward management, preceded the examination for the Hospital certificate; and this in turn was followed by the final state examination.[7]

By 1950 there were three teachers at the Preliminary Training School and a further four full-time tutors in the main School.[8] However the School continued to rely on assistance from members of the medical staff, and the introduction of study days further increased the number of lectures required from them. In 1952 the Hospital decided to abandon its long-standing custom of appointing individual doctors as lecturers to the nursing students, and agreed that the work of lecturing and examining should be shared between all the medical staff on a rota basis.[9]

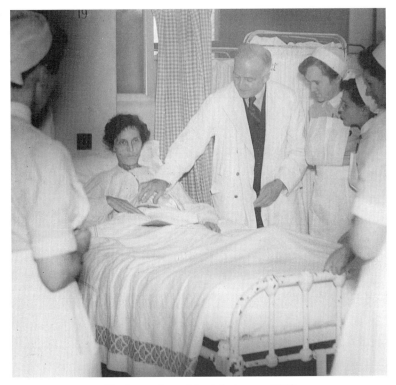

The first ward round for student nurses, 1950.

Joan Loveridge and the Governors still wished to introduce the block system as soon as possible, fearing the effects of further delay on the Hospital's ability to attract students. Nevertheless the study days were judged a success. Many nurses had long looked forward to their introduction and welcomed them enthusiastically. Sisters had to run their wards and departments with reduced numbers of students; this caused some initial ill-feeling but most cooperated as best they could.[10] In 1951 the Sisters successfully petitioned for study days of their own. There was even a feeling that occasional study days were 'more in keeping with the spirit and methods of the Hospital' than the block system used elsewhere. In 1953 Winifred Hector, the Principal Tutor, wrote that she found the block system 'not superficially attractive . . . to spend four or six weeks a year in the classroom is not what moved our students to take up nursing'.[11]

However, when the General Nursing Council published a new syllabus in 1954 St Bartholomew's had to extend its teaching programme. The Council's requirements had become more stringent than in its early days and

Nurses in the classroom, 1951.

Bart's could no longer assume that its own curriculum was necessarily in advance of the Council's standard. Further lectures were needed in bacteriology, child health, psychiatry and social aspects of disease, which could not be accommodated within the existing study days. A modified version of the block system was therefore introduced. Six study days towards the end of a nurse's first year were followed by one months's 'block' in each of her second and third years and six more study days for revision before her final examinations. In total she was to spend 56 days in the classroom in the course of three years after leaving the Preliminary Training School.[12] The scheme was later modified on a number of occasions, with the provision of more periods of study, but the principles of the block system remained in use for more than a quarter of a century. At first the teaching staff found it a challenge to have students under tuition for a continuous period and to retain their interest over several weeks of study, but it was soon realised that the system provided greater opportunities for educational planning and the Principal Tutor found herself arguing for further increases in teaching time. Inevitably there was tension between the needs of patients and the

St. Bartholomew's Hospital Nurses' Training Plan

The block system: outline of revised timetable, 1959/60.

educational requirements of the students who formed much of the nursing workforce, and her requests for additional classroom teaching were frequently opposed by the Assistant Matrons responsible for assigning students to the wards.[13]

By the 1950s long-serving Sisters could detect a marked change in working relationships. As in other hospitals, student nurses were permitted a more relaxed attitude to their superiors than in pre-war years and Sisters felt that they had to be less strict. Many of the rituals and regulations of the 1930s had disappeared during the Second World War, when the increased workload had made it impossible to maintain them, and Joan Loveridge discouraged the customary deference and formality which previous Matrons had insisted on. Nurses were allowed to sit in the Square, though not as yet to eat there, and going to the dining room out of uniform was permitted on days off.[14] However the student nurses of the 1950s and 1960s saw things differently: one former student wrote that 'we lived in a strictly disciplined environment [although] our superiors never tired of telling us how much more strict the discipline had been in their day'.[15] The Hospital authorities gave them a little more freedom than their predecessors, but their hours seemed long and their lives constricted in comparison with those of other skilled workers or students preparing for other professions. Late passes were needed if they wished to be out of the Hospital after 10.30 p.m. Student nurses no longer had to mend the ward linen or run Sister's bath, but they were still expected to prepare breakfast and afternoon tea for the patients and to clean lockers and bedpans. At Hill End there were very few domestic staff and until 1961 it remained the students' task to sweep the floors in the wards.[16]

First names were never used except between friends: in the wards, students and fourth-year 'blue belts' were addressed as 'Nurse', while staff nurses in pink were called 'Miss Smith' or 'Miss Jones'. To the student nurses of that time it still seemed that Sisters reigned with totalitarian authority and the personality of a Sister dominated the atmosphere of a ward. It was in the nurses' perception of her fairness in allocating work and off-duty time, and of the support they could expect in a crisis, that a Sister's

A nurse making tea, 1961.

88

behaviour had most effect on the morale of her subordinates. Unfortunately sarcasm and scorn were still directed at new students by a few of the older Sisters, and on some wards a nurse talking to a patient was considered to be 'doing nothing' and could expect a scolding. By the 1960s, however, most wards had ceased to be run in this way. The few Sisters who acted like this were known to the students, and those sent to work under them could always rely on the sympathy of their more fortunate colleagues.[15]

The need to bring nurses' hours more into line with those of other workers had been addressed by a government report in 1947,[17] and during the 1950s and 1960s the working hours of most Bart's nurses were reduced, with the phased introduction of an eight-hour day. In the 1950s staff nurses were generally able to work either from 7.30 a.m. to 4.30 p.m. or from 4 p.m. until just after midnight, the latter being known as 'twilight duty'. Staff nurses did not as a rule work at nights. Until the early 1960s, however, student nurses still worked either 'days' (7.30 a.m. to 8 p.m.) or 'nights' (8 p.m. to 8 a.m.), with time off during those hours. Their average working week was from 44 to 46 hours and they undertook three months of night duty in each year of training. Most wards still had only students on duty during the hours of darkness, after the 'twilight' staff nurse had left. Though night duty continued as a single long shift, improved daytime hours for students were introduced in 1961–2, with two separate eight-hour shifts and a changeover in the early afternoon.[18]

New trends were also evident in the provision of accommodation for nursing staff. For centuries it had been the tradition that all Sisters and nurses lived within the Hospital, but even before the Second World War some of the specialist departments had begun to employ staff who lived elsewhere.[19] Winifred Hector noted that 'when the first Ward Sister lived out of the Hospital in the 1940s it caused a lot of talk and misgivings'. After the war, however, many more lived out and by 1953 the Clerk to the Governors was suggesting that senior nurses should be encouraged to move out in order to release on-site accommodation for students.[20] By then the Hospital was again suffering from a shortage of accommodation. The increase in staff numbers meant that there were no longer enough rooms in Queen Mary's Home and in the mid 1950s nurses were housed in Bryanston Square and Maybury Mansions, St Marylebone, and also in Charterhouse Chambers near the Hospital. At Maybury Mansions a Sister could rent a flat for her own use, which gave her something of the independence enjoyed by other professional women.

No further accommodation was available on the Hospital site until 1961 when a new nurses' home was opened on the east side of Little Britain. Named Gloucester House in honour of the President of the Hospital, the

Duke of Gloucester, it initially contained about 130 rooms as well as a swimming pool, recreation hall, sun lounge and coffee bar. Although by the 1960s most senior staff preferred to live out some still chose to reside in the Hospital and when Gloucester House opened many of its rooms were occupied by Sisters and staff nurses. Students were obliged to be resident and most were accommodated in Queen Mary's Nurses' Home. The two rooms in the basement of Queen Mary's Home, which had been occupied by the Training School since 1929, remained in use, but on the eleventh floor of Gloucester House a new lecture hall, demonstration room, classroom and library were provided for the School. The Queen Elizabeth II Wing, a new building with specialist theatres and wards for neurosurgery, thoracic, ophthalmic and ear, nose and throat surgery, was formally opened on the same day as Gloucester House, and its completion enabled the departments still based at Hill End to return to Bart's after more than twenty years in Hertfordshire.[21]

Although St Bartholomew's still relied heavily on student labour, there were also about 250 state registered nurses working in the Hospital in the early 1960s. The proportion of registered nurses in the workforce had risen from 19% in 1938 to 37% in 1961. In that year Bart's employed 683 nurses, of whom almost two-thirds were students.[22] During the 1960s staff numbers increased but the number of beds remained roughly constant at 820 or 830. In 1967 there were 838 nursing staff, exclusive of tutors in the Training School,[23] and for the first time in its history Bart's could claim to employ one nurse for every bed. Nursing salaries accounted for about one-fifth of the Hospital's total expenditure.

In 1961 there were 74 Sisters and by 1967 their numbers had grown to 81.[24] Their lives had become rather different from the cloistered routine of forty years earlier when Sisters hardly ever left their wards. In the 1960s two-thirds of the Sisters lived out of the Hospital, either in flats in Maybury Mansions or in their own accommodation. A Sister who lived in Maybury Mansions would travel to work by public transport or might drive to the Hospital if she had a car. She would arrive before 8 a.m., change into uniform, take the night nurse's report and then go to the Sisters' dining room for breakfast before starting work. Her duties in the ward had become ever more demanding. Patients were less likely to be confined to bed and their visitors were more numerous than in previous years and less inclined to defer to Hospital rules. Drug treatments and other medical and surgical techniques were becoming increasingly complex. There was practically no moment, except at night and in the early morning, when there were no medical staff or other visitors in the ward. However Sisters were still expected to be on duty for most of the day. They had to be constantly

Sister Henry Butlin in her sitting room, 1961.

accessible to patients and their relatives, to medical staff and students, or to nurses needing guidance or instruction, and they had come to expect a working pattern of frequent interruptions.

As their responsibilities increased, Sisters also found that they had more paperwork to complete and a growing number of other administrative duties to perform. Since they had no offices, these tasks were done at a desk in the ward. However they still had their sitting rooms to which they could retreat when the pressures of work allowed. This room was very much Sister's private domain, and other nurses did not enter unless invited. Because their hours were long Sisters valued the facility of a room of their own, and when the Queen Elizabeth II Wing was opened in 1961 sitting rooms were provided in every ward, the architect commenting that this was a 'special requirement' of St Bartholomew's.[25]

Like their predecessors, the Sisters of the early 1960s had a working day whose hours were fixed by custom rather than written contract. They were able to use their discretion to stop work when they felt that they could safely do so. In practice a Sister usually worked until 8 or 8.30 p.m. and her hours were considerably longer than those of her nurses. If she were traditionally minded, she would probably read prayers on the ward before she left in the evening. During the 1960s, however, the extension of visiting hours and the introduction of radio and television into the wards made it increasingly difficult for prayers to be heard, and although never formally abolished the custom was abandoned by the end of the decade.[26]

There can have been little doubt of the need to provide further assistance for Ward Sisters. During the 1950s staff nurses in pink had worked mainly in the operating theatres and the out-patient departments, but in the early 1960s the 'pinks' responsible for theatres were regraded as Sister to give them parity with similar posts in other hospitals, and at about the same time 'pinks' were appointed to the general wards where they soon came to be regarded as Sisters' deputies. After 1960 some of the most demanding wards were allowed two Sisters, one senior to the other. Kenton, a children's ward, was the first to have two Sisters.[27] Ten years later most wards still had only one but Vicary, W. G. Grace, Kenton and Lucas each had two Sisters, and Martha and Elizabeth, the obstetric wards, had seven between them. These changes helped Sisters by relieving some of the pressures of their workload, but in the longer term the sharing of responsibility may also have served to weaken the sense of personal commitment that a Sister had traditionally felt towards her ward.

Until the 1960s all sterilising of instruments was done by nurses on the wards. Every ward had a steriliser in which glass syringes, needles and instruments could be boiled for re-use. The nurses also cut dressings from long rolls of gauze and wool, packed them and placed them in drums for sterilisation. However by 1961 it was generally accepted that water boilers and dressing drums could not provide the highest standard of sterility, and in that year the Hospital began a trial scheme with sterile packs containing dressings and disposable instruments issued from a central department. Nurses had to be trained in the correct methods of handling and opening the packs but were relieved of the task of sterilisation. The trial scheme served seven wards and most of the theatres,[28] but in January 1964 the services of the Central Sterile Supplies Department were extended throughout the Hospital and the sterilisers were removed from the wards.

For many years teaching on the wards had been the responsibility of the Sisters and to a lesser extent of the staff nurses. Students were given a list of procedures which they were expected to practise, and Sisters marked the lists when the students moved on to another ward. By 1960 Sisters were also expected to discuss with each student the content of the report which they sent to the Training School. However they were able to set their own

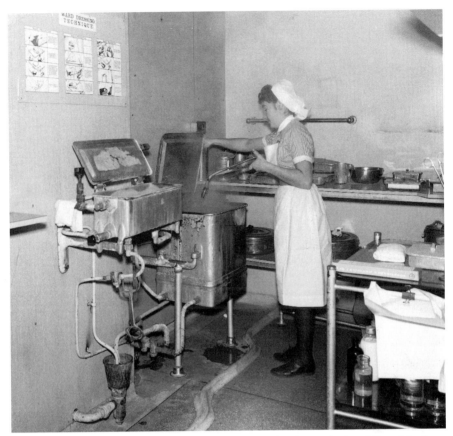

Nurse using a steriliser in Waring Ward, on the last day before the introduction of Central Sterile Supplies in January 1964. The large steriliser was used for trays and bowls, the small one on the left for instruments.

standards in tuition and students often learnt different methods in different wards. Some Sisters were undoubtedly more thorough than others, and many were conscious that in the limited time available they could not provide all the teaching that students on their ward might need. However in the early 1960s St Bartholomew's, like many hospitals, was able to make improvements in clinical teaching. The 'pinks', newly arrived on the wards, had the ability to supervise student nurses and offer them practical instruction. The change to an eight-hour working day for students created a period in the early afternoon when two shifts were in the ward simultaneously, and where possible the opportunity was taken to use this time for tuition. The establishment of Central Sterile Supplies also reduced some of the nursing workload and helped to allow additional teaching.[29]

In 1961 the Training School began to place its own instructors in the wards. As an initial experiment a Sister Tutor undertook teaching each morning in two surgical wards where sterile packs were in use. In the following year the first clinical instructors were appointed as full-time teaching staff in the wards. They sought to be accepted as part of the ward team, although their work was directed not to the patients but to the learning requirements of student nurses. As they had no administrative duties they were able to teach largely without interruption, giving practical tuition at the bedside to nurses selected by the Ward Sister. Although their arrival did not supersede the teaching role of Sisters, it allowed the School to introduce an element of uniformity and to exercise some control over the quality of instruction in the wards. The clinical teachers found that they had to be sensitive to Sisters' authority, and at first some Sisters did not welcome the prospect of a teacher working in their ward. For several years after 1962 there were only two clinical teachers, allocated to a limited number of wards and working for one or two days a week in each. The School did not try to impose teachers on the wards, but as they became established many Sisters who worked with them came to value their presence. Their arrival was also welcomed by the student nurses who generally found them very supportive. By the end of the decade their numbers had increased from two to eight.[30]

In January 1964 the Training School began to use an experimental syllabus which had been formulated by the General Nursing Council in 1962. While previous syllabuses had been largely concerned with the symptoms, treatment and nursing care of diseases, the new course allowed student nurses to study the medical sciences not as isolated subjects but in terms of their effect on individual patients and their nursing needs. The new syllabus was a response to the changing ideas articulated in the 1960s by nurses who wished to be seen as servants of the patient rather than of the doctor. It also set out to achieve a closer integration of theory and practice, with a wider variety of teaching methods and fewer formal lectures.[31] At the time of its introduction Winifred Hector was serving on the committee of the Royal College of Nursing which produced the Platt Report on nurse education, voicing professional aspirations for the independence of training schools from hospitals. Although she did not agree with the whole of the report she found herself in sympathy with much of its outlook, especially its recommendation that nurses in training should be treated as students rather than employees. 'A student', she wrote after the publication of the report in 1964, 'should be in hospital to learn, not to give low-paid service'.[32]

If Winifred Hector's views had changed since the early 1950s, when she had praised the vocational aspect of nursing and expressed doubts about extended study blocks spent in the classroom, this was perhaps a reflection of

Winifred Hector, Principal Tutor 1946–70, teaching a group of student nurses in the early 1960s.

the calibre of the nurses whom she had taught. Leading hospitals such as St Bartholomew's had long been able to attract candidates with an educational record above the average, but in the 1960s Hector became increasingly aware of the improved academic attainments of her students. At a time when some hospitals were having difficulty in finding entrants with a minimum of educational qualifications, up to a third of the candidates whom she accepted for training at Bart's had two or more passes at advanced level in the General Certificate of Education. In 1967 92% of her students passed the state examination, compared with 70% nationally, and at the end of the decade she was able to report that the Hospital had achieved 'a record of examination success that most would envy'.[33]

It had become obvious by the mid 1960s that many of those entering the Training School would have been capable of gaining a place at university. Winifred Hector noted that when she asked such candidates about their career plans 'most said that they wanted above all to be a nurse, but some were a little wistful' about giving up the chance of a university education. She felt that a training school which could recruit well-qualified students should also be able to provide them with the opportunity to obtain a degree at undergraduate level. Degree courses for nurses had existed for many years in the United States and a number of institutions had begun to consider the establishment of similar courses in the United Kingdom. Hector resolved that Bart's should be among the first British hospitals to offer a course leading to both state registration and a university degree. After some ineffectual discussions with the University of London she decided to approach the newly founded City University, formerly the Northampton Polytechnic, in Clerkenwell. She reported that the Registrar enquired whether candidates from Bart's could meet the University's entry requirements 'and was abashed to find that they would easily exceed them'. However she did not believe that the study of nursing had sufficient academic content to reach degree standard without drawing on other subjects, so when the new course was devised in 1967 the nursing elements were combined with City University's standard degree in social science. In this respect it followed the pattern of courses at Edinburgh University and elsewhere, in which nursing was joined with other subjects perceived as more academically demanding.[34]

The first four students started the degree course in 1968. They spent their first year learning practical and theoretical nursing, followed by three years at City University where they studied aspects of sociology, psychology and economics. All social science students at City University undertook a field work project and the Bart's students were to do their field work in the Nursing School studying maternal and child health and psychiatric observation. After graduating at the University they returned to Bart's for four months and then sat their state examination. In the Hospital the degree students benefited from a number of innovations. They were considered to be supernumerary to the staffing establishment and thus could be given more concentrated tuition than other nurses. Their lectures were timed to coincide with ward experience in a relevant subject and they always had a tutor or clinical teacher with them on the wards. These privileges were not shared by other student nurses and gave rise to some resentment, although they were counterbalanced by the hours of study required of nurses on the degree course, which the non-degree students were generally glad to be excused. The course was designed for young women seeking to enter nursing who also wanted to obtain a degree, rather than for those primarily interested in an academic exercise, though there were Ward Sisters who felt that some of the degree students were better at understanding theory than at practical nursing. Nevertheless City University was impressed with its nursing students, not least because they had the advantage of a year's experience of working discipline.[35]

Joan Loveridge retired as Matron in 1967. She came to be remembered as the last Matron of St Bartholomew's, and was certainly the last to wear the traditional black uniform, though not in fact the last to have the title of Matron. Much loved and respected for her kindness and sense of humour, Loveridge had a warm and outgoing personality very different from the severity often expected of hospital Matrons, and admirably filled the role of mother-figure to young nurses.[36] Although she was not a natural leader or innovator, those who worked under her felt that she maintained a good spirit in the Hospital and that Matron and Sisters were mutually supportive. She allowed her staff considerable independence, so that more forward-looking Sisters were able to introduce new practices in their wards while others continued to use the older methods to which they were accustomed.

The new Matron chosen by the Board of Governors was Rhona Jones, formerly Matron of the Bristol Royal Infirmary, who had no previous connection with Bart's and a managerial style very different to that of her predecessor. After her appointment she saw a need to impose greater uniformity of nursing practice and to introduce more modern working methods. In contrast to Loveridge's reports which had spoken of the cherished traditions of patient care handed down to generations of Bart's nurses, Jones suggested to the Hospital's nursing advisory committee that some of the staff she had inherited were insufficiently receptive to new ideas and needed to learn to be self-critical and flexible.[37] She wanted to make rapid changes to whatever she perceived as old-fashioned, and set out to reform many of the distinctive practices which were still valued by some

Formal group of Matron and senior nursing staff. Photograph taken in the Square, to mark the retirement of Joan Loveridge, Matron 1949–67.

longer-serving members of staff. She felt it was unnecessary for wards to be made immaculate for a consultant's round, or for other ward work to stop while the consultant was present, and she attempted, with some success, to eradicate these habits where they had persisted.[38] In 1968 she ended another long-standing custom which she saw as outmoded, the assessment of student nurses for formal 'election' after two or three months on trial. She allowed students in their second and third years, and those in their first year if aged over 21, to live out of the Hospital. Gate hours were abolished for students who lived in. The segregated nurses' dining room was opened to other staff, a cash payment system for meals was introduced and Sisters were given fixed working hours. Such innovations were in line with national trends of the 1960s, and many of them enabled nurses to enjoy a more relaxed lifestyle.

Students reacted favourably to the changes, especially the new freedom to live outside the Hospital, but the response from senior staff was mixed: the abolition of discretionary hours for Sisters was welcomed by some who felt that the old system had discouraged them from taking their full entitlement of off-duty time, but to others it seemed to imply that Sisters were no longer trusted to be conscientious.[39]

The major task facing Rhona Jones was the implementation of the changes proposed in the Salmon Report, which had been published by the Ministry of Health in 1966. Formally titled *The Report of the Committee on Senior Nursing Staff Structure*, it was intended to introduce management principles to the world of nursing and to provide nurses with a status and a career structure comparable to that of other professions. At Bart's as elsewhere the old hierarchy of Matron and Sisters had survived into the 1960s little changed. The Matron by then had a Deputy and a number of Assistant Matrons, but formal reporting structures barely existed and Ward Sisters generally saw themselves as responsible directly to the Matron. However as the Hospital had grown it had become increasingly difficult for the Matron to have a detailed knowledge of all the activities under her jurisdiction and it was scarcely possible for her to supervise them personally. Under the principles of the Salmon Report the most senior post in a large hospital was to be that of Chief Nursing Officer (grade 10) and three tiers of management were to stand between the Chief Nursing Officer and the Ward Sisters on grade 6. This structure was introduced at Bart's in 1969–70. Although Salmon had proposed retaining the title of Matron in appropriate cases, the intention had been to reserve it for certain posts below grade 10,[40] and in the event it fell out of use in most hospitals. The title of Rhona Jones's post was changed to Chief Nursing Officer in 1969. Below her were two Principal Nursing Officers (grade 9), one in charge of operational nursing and one who acted as head of the teaching division. During the 1950s and 1960s training schools had developed a more distinct identity and Winifred Hector had hoped that Salmon would recognise this by giving Principal Tutors an equal status with the former Matrons. If this had occurred it would effectively have freed nursing schools from the Matrons' control, but the Salmon Report failed to meet this expectation. When the Hospital drew up a job specification for the Principal Nursing Officer (teaching division) it followed the Salmon guidelines and stated that in formulating educational policy her role was to assist and advise the Chief Nursing Officer.[41]

Although the Salmon structure offered more career opportunities for nurses, many found it impossible to reconcile the new arrangements with their views on the importance of bedside nursing and the pivotal role of the

Ward Sister. When Brian Salmon, the chairman of the committee which produced the report, came to the Hospital to address the nursing staff many Sisters were disturbed by what he told them. Their traditional autonomy appeared to be threatened and the imposition of a hierarchy of Nursing Officers was perceived as devaluing their role. Many did not want to apply for managerial positions but felt that they were being forced to make an unpalatable choice: seeking promotion would mean losing patient contact, while staying on the wards would entail a loss of independence and the acceptance of closer supervision. The Sisters' dilemma was made no easier by the timing of the reforms. Most had been happy working for Joan Loveridge whose attachment to the traditions of the Hospital had allowed them considerable latitude. The innovations which her successor was making were unpopular with many of the Sisters and the new Chief Nursing Officer had been unable to win their confidence. They closed ranks in opposition to her as well as to the Salmon reforms, and the changes were introduced against a background of considerable ill-feeling within the Hospital.[42]

It soon became clear that in the opinion of many Sisters the new structure offered little incentive to remain in clinical nursing. In 1966 Joan Loveridge had supported the view expressed by Salmon, that the new grade 7 (Nursing Officer) would provide an opportunity for senior Sisters to obtain promotion without forgoing bedside care. A number of Sisters who became Nursing Officers found that they could maintain some patient contact, but others discovered that their work was mainly administrative. A further problem arose because some of the medical staff saw the new grade 7 posts as an obstruction to their traditional relationship with Ward Sisters, while Nursing Officers often felt that doctors were unsupportive.[43] The late 1960s were thus a stressful time both for those who continued as Sisters and those who sought promotion. As many as 64 Sisters gave up their posts between January 1968 and October 1970.[44] The trend for Sisters to be appointed at an earlier age, and to remain in post for a shorter period, had begun before the Salmon Report but was accelerated by the introduction of the new structure. In later years few entrants were to be content with a lifetime career as a Ward Sister.

Another change hastened by the Salmon reforms was a new willingness to appoint senior nursing staff from outside the Hospital. In earlier years very few such appointments had been made. Before the Second World War nurses trained at St Bartholomew's had enjoyed a monopoly of posts in the Hospital, but after 1948 a few staff nurses trained in other countries of the Commonwealth were employed in the out-patient departments. These 'dominion nurses' wore white overalls to distinguish them from nurses who had received their training at Bart's.[45] The first male staff nurse was appointed in 1957,[46] and he too had been trained at another hospital. However until the latter part of the century only nurses who held the Bart's certificate could expect an appointment as Sister. Vacancies were not advertised and no interviews were held. The Matron simply summoned the nurse she had chosen and gave her the job; she was not expected to refuse it. The policy of not appointing outsiders to Sisters' posts was a way of ensuring that traditional standards were maintained, but also arose from a genuine belief that Bart's-trained nurses were second to none. Many hospitals applied a similar system although critics suggested that it made them closed to outside influences and innovative ideas. By the 1960s positions at Bart's had begun to be advertised. Application forms were introduced and job descriptions compiled to replace the Sisters' charges. Although there may still have been a tendency to favour internal candidates, vacancies became open to external competition. A Sister Tutor who had been trained elsewhere was appointed in 1958, and the first male Tutor, the first male Charge Nurse and the first non-Bart's-trained Ward Sister since Isla Stewart's time all arrived in 1965. In 1967, 82 members of staff graded as Sister or above were holders of the Hospital certificate and 19 had been trained elsewhere. While the number of male nurses remained very small, the practice of recruiting staff from outside increased after the appointment of Rhona Jones and the implementation of the Salmon Report, and the percentage of senior staff (Sister and above) who had attended the Training School at Bart's fell from 81% in 1967 to 51% in 1973.[47]

During the 1960s many well-known London hospitals found that they could attract large numbers of students but had difficulty in retaining staff nurses. Students wanted to be trained at a hospital with a first-class reputation but after qualifying often preferred to work nearer home, or to put their names on the books of the growing number of nursing agencies, as an alternative to seeking staff nurse posts in a hospital in central London. Early in the decade the Ministry of Health had responded to the shortage of nurses by encouraging married women to return to nursing as part-time workers. The campaign had met with some success, but hospitals which were not situated in residential areas were at a disadvantage and many had been left with no choice but to employ agency nurses on the agencies' terms. At St Bartholomew's there was considerable anxiety about recruitment but in the 1960s and early 1970s the Hospital was generally able to maintain a full nursing workforce. The obligation for students to remain at work for a fourth year after state registration guaranteed the availability of a reasonable number of staff nurses. Relatively few married and part-time staff were recruited in comparison with most hospitals outside the centre of

London and virtually no agency staff were employed.[48] However by 1973 the shortage of qualified staff had begun to be felt at Bart's and with some reluctance the Hospital began to use the agency services.[49] At first only a few agency nurses were accepted but many more were employed in later years.

As Chief Nursing Officer, Rhona Jones was also concerned about possible difficulties in maintaining student numbers and feared that the continuing use of nurses as unskilled labour might discourage recruitment. Although cleaning had generally ceased to be a task for student nurses after the introduction of ward orderlies in the 1950s, in some wards students still had to clean lockers and cupboards and in the theatres nurses were cleaning equipment and washing walls. After 1967 there were ward clerks to help with messenger duties and routine paperwork, but at first they were few in number and nurses continued to be involved in fetching medical records, unpacking supplies and sundry other clerical tasks.[50] These aspects of nursing were unlikely to appeal to potential candidates at a time when a wider range of other career options was becoming available. Nevertheless St Bartholomew's had few real problems either in recruiting students or in retaining them for the four years needed to gain the Hospital certificate. In 1966 there were about eight enquiries for every place in the Training School and the Matron said that Bart's was fortunate to be able to choose the students it wanted.[51] Inevitably some students dropped out during training and four years later when the Hospital conducted a survey it found that the commonest reasons for leaving were isolation from friends and social life, besides the lack of intellectual stimulation in the work.[52] In fact the wastage

Practical class at the Preliminary Training School, 1966.

Teaching first-year students, 1966.

rate was low in comparison with most other hospitals. In 1966 the national rate of wastage among student nurses was said to be 30% and the average at teaching hospitals 19.9% per annum; at Bart's it was 9.4%. Although this figure increased to 17–18% yearly in 1968–70 the number of students leaving before completing their training remained well below average.[53]

As most of its requirements for nursing personnel could still be supplied by students and registered nurses St Bartholomew's had little need to consider alternative sources of recruitment. Many hospitals used less well-qualified staff to undertake basic nursing tasks but Bart's had been reluctant to follow this trend. The grade of enrolled nurses, or 'assistant nurses' as they were originally known, had existed since the 1940s but like many Matrons in conservative hospitals Helen Dey had refused to employ them, believing that they would dilute high standards of care and lower the prestige of nursing.[54] Even in the 1960s very few enrolled nurses worked at Bart's: there were two on the staff in 1961 and the same number in 1967, though in 1970 eleven were employed and in 1971 thirteen. This was still less than 2% of the total, at a time when in hospitals nationally about 14% of nursing staff were enrolled nurses and a further 8% were pupils in training for enrolment.

Similarly by 1971 unqualified nursing auxiliaries provided 22% of the nursing workforce across the country as a whole, and in many hospitals it was an auxiliary who made beds, changed linen, washed and dressed patients and assisted them with bedpans. At Bart's with its large Training School there was an ample supply of students to undertake routine duties and until the end of the 1960s few auxiliaries were employed. In 1961 there was only one and although by 1971 their numbers had grown to 22 full-time and 3 part-time staff, this still represented only about 3% of the workforce.[55]

A new syllabus for nurse education was designed by the General Nursing Council in 1969 and introduced at Bart's in 1970–1. The new teaching requirements meant a considerable reduction in the amount of time spent by students on the wards. One response to this was a doubling of the number of nursing auxiliaries employed in the Hospital in twelve months between 1971 and 1972.[56] It had also become obvious that more enrolled nurses would be working at Bart's in the future, and in view of this the Hospital decided to begin an enrolled nurse training programme of its own. It was hoped that enrolled nurse pupils who qualified at Bart's could be encouraged to take long-term employment in the Hospital to help fill the gap left by the reduction in student labour and the imminent shortage of staff nurses. The 'Training School for Pupil Nurses' opened in 1971. It was sited initially in Queen Mary's Nurses' Home but later moved to Gloucester House. There were two annual intakes of fifteen pupils; the term 'student nurse' was denied to enrolled nurse trainees. Like all pupil nurse courses it was two years in length and was weighted towards practical training, with a much lower theoretical content than the three-year course which led to state registration. No educational qualifications were required for entry. Some pupils were as young as 18 but most were rather older than the average student nurse and had previous work experience in another occupation. A total of 285 pupils passed successfully through the School in its fifteen years. The course also proved its value as an aid to recruitment: many pupils chose to continue working at Bart's and in the later 1970s a majority of wards had one or two enrolled nurses. Most proved to be reliable workers, and as relatively few had career ambitions they often remained in post for longer than registered nurses.[57]

By the beginning of the 1970s many changes in teaching methods had been introduced. Winifred Hector had taken a special interest in audio-visual teaching aids and was among the first to make full use of them in nurse education in the United Kingdom. The Training School was a pioneer in making tape recordings for educational use and after acquiring a film camera in the late 1960s it made films on many subjects including blood pressure, dressing techniques and various aspects of anatomy and

Making an educational film, 1969.

physiology.[58] For enrolled nurse pupils, as for degree course students, each period of classroom study was followed by a period of related practical experience on a ward or elsewhere. The non-degree course leading to state registration was not yet structured in this way, but student nurses had fewer set lectures and more diversity of teaching than in earlier years. Hector noted in 1970 that many of the consultants' lectures developed into a dialogue rather than a monologue.[59] In accordance with the requirements of the General Nursing Council, a secondment period was offered to all students, either in obstetrics or in psychiatric nursing. Those who took the obstetric option spent three months in the maternity unit at St Bartholomew's, where midwifery training for nurses had been resumed in 1962, or at the Mothers' Hospital in Hackney; the psychiatric secondment was generally at Hill End Hospital, with which Bart's had a long-standing connection.[60]

Until 1971 the Preliminary Training School continued to be based in the countryside. Piggott's Manor at Letchmore Heath offered beautiful surroundings but was felt to be unrealistic as a teaching venue. The staff were isolated from the work of the Hospital and from their colleagues in the main part of the School. The grand rooms of Piggott's Manor bore little resemblance to a hospital and a 36-mile return journey by coach was required for the trainees to visit the wards. In 1971 the Letchmore Heath buildings were closed and accommodation for an eight-week introductory course was provided in Queen Mary's Nurses' Home. The relocation of the course allowed students to become familiar with the wards and other departments of the Hospital from the start of their training.[61]

Student numbers were increasing slowly: before the Second World War the Training School had an annual intake of about 150 and in the 1960s it was still usually accepting fewer than 200 students each year.[62] Nevertheless further tuition was needed to impart the new technical skills required of nurses in the light of recent advances in medicine and surgery, and in the mid 1960s almost 50 members of the consultant staff were involved in nurse education. In 1961, besides the Principal Tutor, there were five Sister Tutors and four further teachers at the Preliminary Training School; by 1971 there was a notional establishment of 23.[63] One of these posts had special responsibility for post-registration training and at the start of the 1970s the School was offering two yearly study days to all Sisters, midwives and staff nurses in pink.[64] Like many other schools of nursing, Bart's often found it difficult to recruit suitable tutors and in 1971 several posts were unfilled,[65] but despite this the size of the teaching staff had doubled in ten years and a marked improvement in the ratio of staff to students had been achieved.

Chapter Six

PROGRESS AND TURMOIL:
ST BARTHOLOMEW'S AFTER 1974

During the first 25 years of the National Health Service St Bartholomew's, like other teaching hospitals, had been able to preserve much of its institutional culture. It had its own Board of Governors responsible to the Minister of Health, and many decisions continued to be made at local level. The reorganisation of the Health Service in 1974 brought an end to local autonomy, and Bart's lost its direct link to the Ministry. The Board of Governors was abolished and most of its powers were transferred to a new City and East London Area Health Authority, which also managed hospitals in the boroughs of Hackney, Tower Hamlets and Newham. The Area Health Authority was subordinate to the North East Thames Regional Health Authority which had responsibility for hospital services in a substantial part of Greater London and Essex.

The post of Chief Nursing Officer ceased to exist in 1974 and Rhona Jones retired on grounds of ill health. Gwendoline Gardiner was appointed as District Nursing Officer of the City and Hackney District of the Area Health Authority. She retired in October 1975 and was replaced by Mary Armstrong. Both came from outside the District. Armstrong was a university graduate trained at St Thomas' Hospital and had worked at the Department of Health and Social Security. As District Nursing Officer she was a member of the District Management Team which had been set up to allow an equal partnership of nurses, doctors and lay administrators. With the new emphasis on consensus in management, senior nurses were given a voice in virtually all decision-making at District level and a seat on most major committees.

The reforms of 1974 also meant that there was no longer an individual postholder at St Bartholomew's who could be identified by staff and patients as successor to the role of the Matron. Since Bart's was the District's largest and most prestigious hospital much of the District Nursing Officer's time was spent there, but she also had responsibility for nurses on seven other sites. These were the Eastern, German, Hackney and Mothers' Hospitals (the former 'Hackney Group'), together with St Leonard's, the Metropolitan and St Mark's. The District's eight hospitals were constituted as two divisions, each with a Divisional Nursing Officer. The Hackney hospitals formed one division while in the other St Bartholomew's was linked with

St Mark's and St Leonard's and with the Metropolitan until its closure in 1977. The Divisional Nursing Officer based at Bart's had management duties at all four hospitals, and like her counterpart in Hackney was answerable to the District Nursing Officer.

The Hospitals in the District had very different origins. Some were former workhouse infirmaries, while others had once been voluntary hospitals dependent on subscriptions and donations. As a specialist institution St Mark's had an international reputation for colo-rectal surgery, but the others were purely local hospitals and many of them had been poorly resourced in the past. Nursing standards were not always high and staffing levels often inadequate. During the late 1970s and early 1980s many of the smaller hospitals were closed in a programme of rationalisation, but in those which remained open the connection with Bart's was undoubtedly beneficial in raising standards and resolving staffing problems.[1]

In nurse education a post was established at the level of Divisional Nursing Officer, with responsibility for teaching throughout the District. The City and Hackney District had inherited three nursing schools: besides the St Bartholomew's Hospital Training School there were the Kingsland School of Nursing (comprising the formerly separate training schools at the Metropolitan and St Leonard's Hospitals) and the Hackney School which used the facilities of the Eastern, German and Hackney Hospitals. It was agreed that these would be merged to form a single District school, based at Bart's and called the St Bartholomew's School of Nursing.[2] The amalgamation was overseen by Helen Collyer, a former gold medallist who had left St Bartholomew's but returned in 1970 to succeed Winifred Hector as head of the Training School.[3] In 1974 she became Director of Nurse Education for the City and Hackney District.

The Kingsland School was the first to be assimilated. It was very small, with a maximum yearly intake of 75 students, and had suffered from a shortage of teaching staff. In 1974 it was rehoused in the former Matron's flat in Queen Mary's Nurses' Home. The teaching programme was altered to coincide with that of the Bart's students and tutors from the two schools began to work interchangeably, sometimes teaching Bart's and Kingsland students together. After 1976 there was no separate intake to the Kingsland School and student nurses entering St Bartholomew's were able to use St Leonard's as well as Bart's for ward experience. Integration of the Hackney School was more complicated as it had an annual intake of up to 180, half of whom were enrolled nurse pupils. Immediate relocation was impossible and the Hackney School continued to function separately for a few years.[4]

Until 1975 admissions to the St Bartholomew's School of Nursing were

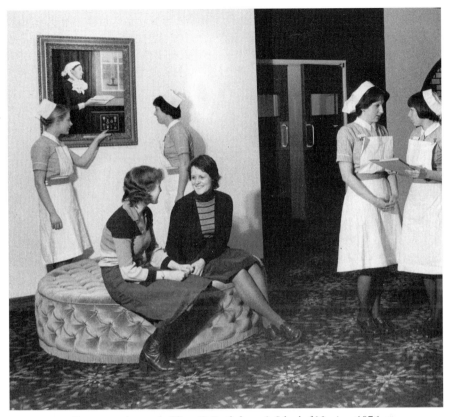

Entrance to the new building, St Bartholomew's School of Nursing, 1976.

effectively limited by the size of the classrooms. No room could seat more than 46, and this had become the maximum figure for each intake. In June 1975 the School moved into new accommodation in an extension to Gloucester House. The building included a lecture theatre seating 120, three large classrooms, a library with over 4000 books and an audio-visual room. Its formal opening by the Duchess of Gloucester took place in March 1976. At first it had been hoped that the new facilities would allow a reduction from four annual intakes to three, but the merger with the Hackney and Kingsland Schools brought a change of plan. In 1976, after the ending of admissions to the Kingsland School, Bart's received five intakes of 50 students. The Hackney School accepted its last entrants in 1977 and in the following year Bart's had six intakes of 55.[5]

Teaching in the early 1970s was still very much hospital-based, although social aspects of nursing were coming to assume a more important place in the syllabus. At the beginning of the decade Bart's had felt unable to offer its students a secondment in community nursing because of the lack of a local population in the City. Community work was still perceived as less skilful and only enrolled nurse pupils were offered practical training, although there was a theoretical course on community nursing for student nurses in their third year, with one day spent visiting public health services.[6] However it was known that community nursing was likely to be an area of rapid growth which would need to be given a new emphasis in nurse education. A community placement scheme for student nurses from Bart's was started on a small scale in Hackney in 1973, and students on maternity secondments could also accompany midwives from the Mothers' Hospital on their home visits.[7]

By the mid 1970s all students were offered two secondment periods, one in obstetrics and the other in psychiatric, geriatric or community nursing. A psychiatric secondment would take them to Hill End or another relatively distant hospital, but all other placements were arranged within the City and Hackney District. After closure of the Hackney School the combined

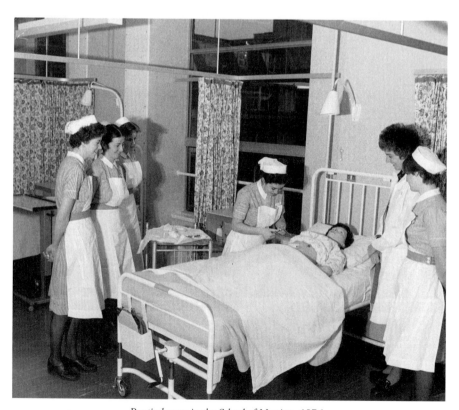

Practical room in the School of Nursing, 1976.

Award of certificate to the first male student nurse at Bart's, 1982.

School of Nursing at Bart's was able to use the facilities of all the hospitals in the District to provide varied ward experience. Inevitably a few difficulties arose, and some of the wards in the Hackney hospitals were in such poor condition that the General Nursing Council would not allow them to be used for training;[8] but in general the students benefited from the breadth of experience in the hospitals of the District and found that it complemented their work in the more specialised wards at Bart's.

Nursing students at St Bartholomew's in the 1970s and 1980s were a more varied body than their predecessors. Before the Second World War it could be assumed that a hospital nurse was white, female and unmarried, and at Bart's this was still the predominant picture throughout the 1950s and 1960s, much longer than at most other hospitals. A few married nurses were employed in the 1960s but in 1967 there were only five married students, less than 1% of the student body. Although men constituted over 10% of the national nursing workforce at the start of the 1970s most worked in psychiatric nursing and at Bart's there were only six male nurses and two male auxiliaries.[9] Male students were not admitted, and until the 1970s there was no consensus within the Hospital that its training facilities should be extended to men. However the Hackney School of Nursing had accepted male students and in 1979, after the amalgamation was completed, the combined School at St Bartholomew's admitted its first male student.

Enrolled nurse pupils, 1977.

The first male pupil nurse arrived shortly afterwards. Although nursing continued to be perceived as primarily a female occupation, the numbers of men slowly increased during the 1980s and by the early 1990s more than one student in ten was male.[10]

A similar change occurred in the mix of ethnic backgrounds of the students. In the 1960s very few came from families with roots overseas. In 1970 it was found that 62% of student and pupil nurses in non-teaching hospitals in Greater London, and 17% in teaching hospitals, had been born outside the United Kingdom;[11] but at Bart's the proportion was much smaller, perhaps because at that time relatively few candidates from overseas had been able to reach the standard required for admission. However, when the second generation of immigrant families came of training age during the 1970s, students began to arrive from a wider range of ethnic groups. The diversity of backgrounds was most apparent among enrolled nurse pupils and at the Hackney and Kingsland Schools. The social climate of the following decades demanded a more positive commitment to equality of opportunity, and in the 1980s a campaign was launched to recruit students from the different ethnic communities within the borough of Hackney. In 1990 Bart's published a statement that it would make no distinction between nursing students on grounds of creed, race, age, class or gender.[12]

The Hospital had long seen itself as a centre of excellence. Students were taught that for a Bart's nurse only the very highest standards were acceptable, and that the quality of nursing at St Bartholomew's set an example to others in the profession. However for many years belief in the importance of high standards had been combined with a natural conservatism and a reluctance to abandon long-standing conventions. In the 1970s and 1980s these attitudes were increasingly challenged. Many who came to work at Bart's, particularly on the administrative staff, saw the history and traditions of the Hospital as an irrelevance if not an encumbrance. Most managers accepted the corporate culture that had grown up in the National Health Service and perceived that excellence lay not in tradition but in innovation. At the same time growing demands were made by the Department of Health and the Regional Health Authority, both for the implementation of new management practices and for continuing reductions in expenditure. The apparent stability which Bart's nurses had known in the past was replaced by a climate in which reform and restructuring became the norm, budgets were ever more tightly constrained, and job specifications and reporting lines at senior level were constantly changing.

These trends were evident throughout the National Health Service but were especially conspicuous at hospitals such as Bart's where long-established traditions had prevailed. Many nurses did not find it easy to come to terms with the changes, although the desire for continuity was naturally strongest among those who had worked at Bart's for many years. It was this group which provided the most active support for the League of Nurses and strove to keep in touch with past generations and former colleagues. A number of Sisters endeavoured to maintain some of the customs of an earlier age and continued to provide ward teas and floral displays on the annual View Day, though inevitably as time passed these became less impressive and in many wards ceased altogether. While the sense of tradition was much less pervasive than in earlier years it did not wholly disappear and even recent entrants continued to be aware of the Hospital's distinctive identity. In 1975 one student nurse wrote of the ceremony in the eighteenth-century Great Hall at which the Hospital certificates and Clothworkers' prizes were presented: 'These occasions have a special air and emotion about them, a feeling that you are part of something which has existed for centuries . . . I felt a sense of both pride and humility in being part of it'.[13]

Nursing practices, on the other hand, were increasingly assimilated to those found elsewhere in the National Health Service. Circulars from the Department of Health regulated many areas of activity. Long-serving Sisters who had never been asked to sign a contract of employment were issued with job descriptions after perhaps twenty years in post. The grade of 'staff nurse in pink', once seen as characteristic of Bart's, came to be viewed as superfluous because it did not exist in other parts of the Health Service, and the numbers of pinks employed in the Hospital gradually diminished. The rules and etiquette of previous decades were also swept away and in an age of informality nurses began to call Sisters by their first names. The old custom of referring to a Sister by the title of her ward fell out of favour, and while some staff might still speak of 'Sister Rahere' or 'Sister Percival Pott', to others this seemed distinctly old-fashioned. On the wards, Sisters generally felt that they no longer needed a private sitting room; these rooms were gradually opened to staff nurses and others, and effectively became ward offices. For many nurses, a Sister's post had become merely a step on a career ladder which might involve frequent moves from one hospital to another in the course of a working life.

Tensions between custom and innovation were also reflected in the changing attitudes to nurses' uniforms. Some nurses wished to maintain the traditional standard of dress while others felt that in the changed conditions of the late twentieth century stringent regulations were unnecessary. The result was inevitably a compromise. Cardigans, once banned, were first permitted underneath a cloak for outdoor wear and later became almost universally acceptable. Student nurses were no longer required to wear uniform during periods of classroom study, and many nurses in managerial positions ceased wearing uniform even on formal occasions. However, despite a growing opinion in many hospitals that traditional uniform was too reminiscent of Victorian domestic service, Bart's was reluctant to abandon it. The wearing of uniform continued to be obligatory in almost every ward,[14] and after 1974 a plan to alter its distinctive colours was reversed by the District Management Team and the Bart's uniform was introduced in the other hospitals of the City and Hackney District. Changes were devised to make the uniform more practical and comfortable, and during the 1980s aprons and caps ceased to be worn, but the belts and colours of the characteristic Bart's uniform survived into the early 1990s.

Although increasing numbers of nurses were employed in specialist departments, the ward was still the place of work for the majority of nursing staff. By the last quarter of the twentieth century most wards were busier than ever before. Demands for increased productivity and fuller use of resources brought continuing reductions in the patient's average length of stay and a rapid growth in turnover. Earlier discharge of convalescent patients meant higher average dependency levels in the ward, and generated more administrative work as well as a need for more intensive nursing. These changes, together with the constant influx of visitors, made it impossible for Ward Sisters to maintain a fixed timetable of the kind formerly used to regulate nurses' duties. The old arrangement whereby each consultant's patients occupied a single ward, or pair of adjoining wards, was

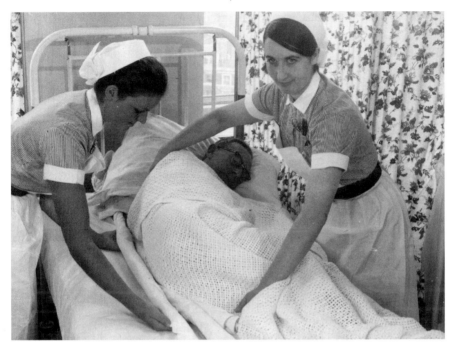

Bedmaking, 1970s.

also breaking down and in some parts of the Hospital had been largely abandoned. In many wards the beds were divided between several consultants and were reallocated at frequent intervals. The close working relationships which had once existed between Sisters and individual consultants became difficult to sustain, while growing numbers of house officers and medical students, many of them unfamiliar with the ward and in need of guidance, placed further demands on the nursing staff. Another kind of long-term working relationship had already disappeared when ward maids, floor cleaners and orderlies had ceased to form part of the Ward Sister's team and were placed under the control of the Domestic Department; the new arrangement made it easier to move domestic staff around the Hospital in order to achieve economies in the efficient use of labour. Nevertheless Sisters found that they had more responsibility for staff management, partly resulting from the arrival of new grades such as enrolled nurses, auxiliaries and ward clerks, but also because of the increased complexity of staffing rotas as working hours became shorter.

In 1981 Sylvia Docking, previously a Senior Nursing Officer in the School of Nursing, was appointed Director of Nurse Education; and in the following year Pamela Hibbs, a former Ward Sister and Senior Nursing

Officer in charge of night duty, became District Nursing Officer.[15] Her appointment coincided with a reorganisation of the National Health Service, when Area Health Authorities were replaced by smaller bodies and a new City and Hackney District Health Authority was established. The former divisions within the District were reconstituted as 'Units', with St Bartholomew's and St Mark's in one Unit and the Hackney hospitals in another. The District Health Authority continued the policy of its predecessor in closing smaller hospitals and in planning a new general hospital at Homerton, which was intended to replace them. When the Homerton Hospital opened in 1986 it became the centrepiece of the Hackney Unit. The new hospital had its own nursing staff but also provided ward experience for students at the St Bartholomew's School of Nursing.

In the early 1980s a new system of nursing practice, originally developed in the United States, was introduced into the hospitals of the City and Hackney District. The 'nursing process', with its analytical framework of assessing needs, setting care objectives and evaluating results, was intended to provide a convincing theoretical basis for nursing activity. Like many hospitals, St Bartholomew's had made several attempts in the 1960s and 1970s to move away from task-based patient care. It had long been accepted that giving nurses a series of repetitive tasks was less satisfactory than making them responsible for a particular group of patients, but moves towards 'patient assignment' or 'total patient care' had been only partially successful because job allocation was invariably easier to organise in a busy ward. The nursing process laid similar emphasis on the value of individualised care but its systematic approach also made it attractive to nurses seeking higher standards of professionalism. The Health Authority endorsed a well-publicised programme to implement the nursing process in every ward. Initial reactions were varied: some nurses found difficulty with the amount of documentation required but others welcomed a system which gave them greater responsibility and opportunity for initiative.[16] As the nursing process became more established variant approaches were developed and Sisters were able to choose the model which they felt most appropriate to the needs of their ward. These changes brought a new perception of the role of nurses and helped them to establish their professional identity. Nurses also began to recognise that if their function was to collect and analyse information, to assess health needs and devise care plans, they would require skills in problem-solving and critical thinking as well as a sound knowledge base. The General Nursing Council recommended that the educational syllabus should incorporate the concept of the nursing process, and the St Bartholomew's School of Nursing introduced it to the curriculum to coincide with its implementation in the wards.

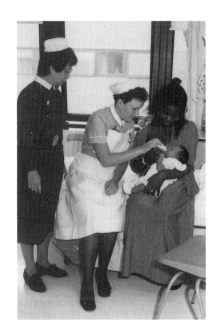

A second-year student nurse on a midwifery
placement at Homerton Hospital, c.1988.

In 1986 the Clothworkers' prizes for the best examination results were replaced by bursaries awarded to nurses wishing to undertake further study after registration.[17] In the same year the School developed a new registered nurse programme, with the first students starting the course in October 1987. To reduce the need for repetitive teaching there were four annual intakes instead of six, with a larger number of students in each. Theory and practice of nursing were studied in conjunction with other relevant topics: these included sociology, psychology, ethics and health education, subjects relatively new to the curriculum, besides long-established areas of study such as physiology. A total of 34 wards and departments and 11 community health centres in the District were used for practical experience. Students were still expected to undertake some night duty but the requirement was reduced from twenty weeks to eight. They were assessed throughout the course and completed six written examination papers and eight pieces of coursework.[18]

The prestige of the Bart's examination and certificate had long been jealously preserved, although in the mid 1970s the requirement for a compulsory fourth year of service was abolished and the certificate came to be granted at the same time as registration. The new registered nurse programme brought further changes. Although originally devised to lead to a certificate, it was validated as a diploma course by City University in May 1990. No students had yet completed the programme, but validation

117

enabled those who finished the course in the winter of 1990–1 to obtain a Diploma in Nursing Studies from the University if the standard of their work was sufficiently high. It was agreed that a Bart's certificate could be awarded to existing students whose passes were not of diploma standard, but after 1990 new students were accepted only for diploma-level study and ceased to be eligible for the certificate. Possession of the diploma secured automatic admission to the register, which meant that students no longer had to sit a separate examination for state registration. The introduction of the diploma also brought changes to the annual award ceremony, and from 1991 students wore academic dress at the ceremony instead of uniform.[19]

Susan Studdy was appointed Director of Nurse Education in 1987. Previously an Assistant Director, she had been responsible for planning the curriculum of the new registered nurse programme. Her first years in office were a period of considerable activity when it became clear that there were to be major national changes in education, affecting both the content of courses and the organisational status of nursing schools. The St Bartholomew's School of Nursing was extended and refurbished in 1988–9, and in April 1989 it merged with the former Mothers' Hospital midwifery school to become the St Bartholomew's College of Nursing and Midwifery. The title of Director of Nurse Education was changed to Principal, and forty students and five teachers transferred from the Mothers' to the new College.[20] After successive amalgamations the student body had grown to over 900, but in the late 1980s student numbers were falling nationally and the College decided to implement a planned reduction to about 540. This was almost exactly the same figure as in 1971, although by the end of the 1980s there had been a substantial increase in students on post-basic courses.[21] The tutorial staff continued to expand: in 1975 there were 24, of whom eight were clinical teachers, but by 1989 the College had 63 funded teaching posts besides librarians, audio-visual technicians and secretarial staff. With reduced numbers of students on pre-registration courses, one tutor was employed for every eleven students, while the national average in the late 1980s was 1:17.[22]

The degree course established in the 1960s continued in its original form until 1988 when the last intake of students was accepted. Its separation of the degree component from the nursing elements, though characteristic of early degree programmes, was no longer felt to be satisfactory and the course was redesigned to integrate the study of nursing with other subjects. The first students started the new course in October 1989. It was a little shorter than its predecessor, leading in exactly four years to a City University bachelor's degree in Nursing and Human Sciences. The course content emphasised health promotion as well as health care, and students were

College brochure, 1989.

expected to acquire knowledge of social and physical sciences before undertaking detailed study of illness and nursing interventions. The course was felt to be demanding in comparison both with others at the College and with many degree courses elsewhere. Besides writing a dissertation, students on the new course sat three times as many examination papers as other student nurses at Bart's and were required to complete almost five times as much assessed coursework. They attended for 40 weeks in each year, instead of 30 weeks expected of most university students, and had a total of 75 weeks' supernumerary clinical experience in the City and Hackney District.[23]

Degree students enjoyed the benefit of a full-time education as they were not considered part of the nursing workforce. However all other students at the College were employees of the District Health Authority and their education remained to some extent incidental to their duties in the District's hospitals. The pattern of multiple annual intakes of students was also largely dictated by operational and practical requirements and had no clear educational purpose. In the mid 1980s St Bartholomew's, like other hospitals, was still dependent on its nursing school to maintain its manpower levels, though students formed a smaller proportion of the workforce than in the earlier part of the century. Their supernumerary periods had been progressively extended and in 1987 were increased from 30% to 60% of the pre-registration course.[24]

Many educationalists had long opposed the subordination of training needs to service functions, and by the 1980s nurses had become increasingly aware that no other profession trained its entrants in this way. In 1986 the United Kingdom Central Council for Nursing, Midwifery and Health Visiting, as successor to the General Nursing Councils, published a report entitled *Project 2000: a new preparation for practice*. It proved to be a far-reaching review, touching almost every aspect of nurse education, and one of its aims was to separate educational activity from the need to provide a service to patients. The report proposed that student nurses would cease to be hospital employees and would be paid a non-means-tested grant rather than a salary. The first Project 2000 courses were to begin in 1989 and were to be professionally accredited by the English National Board for Nursing and Midwifery, and academically validated by a university or the Council for National Academic Awards. At Bart's this framework was already in place for the existing diploma programme, and plans were made to begin a Project 2000 course in October 1990, with two intakes each year in spring and autumn. With the District Health Authority no longer responsible for their remuneration, student nurses were to be supernumerary for 80% of the course and their 27 weeks of rostered service were to be educationally led. However the Department of Health announced that funding would not be available in 1990 and the arrival of the first Project 2000 students had to be postponed until April 1991.[25]

Project 2000 enabled the College of Nursing and Midwifery to introduce a modular system of learning. For enrolled nurse pupils and degree students it had been possible to relate ward experience to classroom teaching by means of a concurrent programme, but until the late 1980s Bart's had not been able to do this for non-degree students on pre-registration courses. Their study blocks had been reorganised in 1979 and again in 1981–2 but service priorities meant that little correlation of theory and practice had been possible. In 1987 the study blocks were replaced by 'units of learning' and a more thorough attempt was made at matching classroom time to clinical experience, but only with the start of Project 2000 was it possible to establish a comprehensive programme of training modules in which teaching and clinical placement were systematically related. All Project 2000 courses were to have an eighteen-month common foundation programme, followed by eighteen months' specialisation in adult, children's, mental health or mental handicap nursing. The College decided to offer the first three of these options, with education in mental health nursing being provided for the first time. Students who met the required standards were to be awarded a City University diploma, as evidence of their qualification to practise in both hospital and community settings.

The Project 2000 reforms also envisaged a single level of registered nurse and as a result the training of enrolled nurses was discontinued nationally in 1990. At St Bartholomew's this change had been anticipated and the pupil nurse course ended in 1986.[26] A conversion programme for enrolled nurses wishing to seek registration was begun in 1990. Nurses who completed this course were given a Bart's certificate, which continued to be awarded for the conversion programme even after its discontinuance as a qualification for new entrants.

As longer-term aims the United Kingdom Central Council proposed that all teachers in schools of nursing should be university graduates and that facilities should be improved to the standard of other institutions of higher education. By 1992 about half of the tutors at St Bartholomew's were graduates and most others were studying for a degree.[27] With the development of nursing science as a discipline separate from medicine, and the increased availability of competent nurse tutors, the need to employ medical lecturers largely disappeared. In the early 1980s Hospital consultants were still making a substantial contribution to the education of nurses but under the 1987 programme their involvement was reduced and with the introduction of Project 2000 consultant staff ceased to be employed as teachers on pre-registration courses.

Both the removal of students from the Ward Sister's team and the new perception of the nurse's role as a coordinator depended on the availability of other workers to whom routine tasks could be delegated. Nursing auxiliaries had come to Bart's in increasing numbers during the 1970s and 1980s and when Project 2000 began to be implemented they already formed a significant part of the workforce. By then the Hospital's traditional reluctance to employ lower-level ward staff had largely been forgotten. As part of the Project 2000 changes the National Health Service Training Authority proposed a new grade of health care assistant, specifically trained to assist in clinical procedures and observations. It was expected that half of the additional staff needed to replace student labour would be care assistants, and in June 1991 the College of Nursing and Midwifery began a programme of practical training for support workers in this category.[28]

In common with other schools and colleges of nursing, St Bartholomew's was able to develop a wide range of continuing education opportunities in the last quarter of the twentieth century. Seminars, study days and short in-service training courses were provided; topics included health education, patient dependency and management development, as well as a variety of clinical subjects. With a growing number of nurses wishing to pursue a specialisation, extended post-basic courses in stomatherapy, intensive care nursing, renal nursing and family planning were started in the 1970s and quickly became popular. In 1980 the stoma care course had an eighteen-month waiting list. By 1987 Bart's offered six post-registration courses leading to an English National Board certificate.[29] Following the move of the continuing education department to enlarged accommodation in Gloucester House in 1989, further rapid expansion of post-basic education became possible. Within two years another six English National Board clinical courses were started, including courses on neonatal special care and on nursing patients with AIDS. An eighteen-month post-registration midwifery course, with both hospital and community experience in the City and Hackney District, was approved in July 1990; and in the following autumn a modular course was launched, in cooperation with City University, which gave postgraduate students the option of working for a master's degree in Nursing Studies.[30]

Research work on nursing subjects began to be undertaken at Bart's in the early 1980s. The first initiatives were taken by senior nurses working in the City and Hackney District rather than by teaching staff. Following several years of local effort to reduce the incidence of pressure sores in elderly patients, a research programme was commissioned in 1982 by the District Nursing Officer, Pamela Hibbs. The work was funded by the joint research board of the Hospital and Medical College, and later by the Regional

Health Authority. Particular emphasis was given to orthopaedic patients, who had been found to be especially prone to sores, and several papers were published.[31] A further research project by District staff investigated distress symptoms in terminally-ill patients.[32] By the end of the decade the College of Nursing and Midwifery was expressing an interest in becoming a research base but, as in many nursing schools, progress was difficult because staff lacked opportunities to develop skills and confidence. Most found that they had longer hours of student teaching than academic staff in universities whom they might have wished to emulate. Nevertheless in the early 1990s research work was being undertaken on a number of topics, including issues relating to educational development, problem-solving and ethical decision-making.[33]

For many years Bart's had enjoyed a consistently high reputation for the quality of its nursing care, but until the 1980s quality standards in hospitals had been largely subjective. By 1985 new management practices in the National Health Service, and a changed social climate which valued objective consumer information, were leading health authorities to create frameworks for systematic quality assessment on the model of those which existed in the United States. In the City and Hackney District Pamela Hibbs as District Nursing Officer was made responsible for establishing a multi-faceted quality assurance programme. In 1986 'quality circles' were introduced and patient satisfaction surveys undertaken on three wards. Other initiatives built on the work already in progress on monitoring of pressure sores. A more complex task was the search for suitable criteria for scientific evaluation of the quality of patient care. By 1987 almost half of English health authorities were using a derivative of a criteria set called 'Monitor', based on a package developed in America in the 1970s. The Quality of Care Unit in the City and Hackney District rejected Monitor, which was not felt to reach the standard required for a continuing programme, and began to develop its own assessment tools. By the end of the decade the District was using a model similar to the Dynamic Standard Setting system promoted by the Royal College of Nursing, although trials of other packages continued.[34] The first quality assurance systems were primarily concerned with nursing standards, though other approaches were also encouraged; but further commitments to quality programmes were made in government legislation of 1990 and in the 'Patients' Charter' promulgated by the Department of Health in 1991, and later initiatives at Bart's, as in other hospitals, were increasingly directed towards multi-disciplinary clinical audit.

Clinical directorates, introduced throughout the National Health Service in the late 1980s and early 1990s, were another example of change made

Using a computer in Percival Pott Ward, late 1980s.

under the influence of American practice. This form of management structure was first adopted at Guy's Hospital, where its advantages were perceived by doctors who had studied an American model. For nurses it served to resolve a dilemma which had been apparent since the reforms of 1974. In the City and Hackney District, Nursing Officers (grade 7) normally managed a group of wards or departments with linked clinical specialities, but at a more senior level responsibility was divided on a geographical basis. After 1982 the Divisional Nursing Officers were replaced by Unit Directors of Nursing Services, each still responsible for nurses on specific hospital sites, but there was increasing acceptance of the benefits of ignoring geography and focusing on clinical speciality for all nurse managers. When a clinical directorate structure was established in 1990, the Unit posts disappeared and nurse management was assimilated to clinical specialities across the District. Each directorate was headed by a consultant, who was assisted by a senior nurse and a service manager; a typical directorate was responsible for three wards and two out-patient clinics, functioning at the Homerton Hospital as well as St Bartholomew's.[35]

The introduction of the new structure proved a difficult time for many of those involved. The District's financial problems were worsening, some of the new Clinical Directors felt inadequately prepared for the management of change, and for the nursing staff the reforms necessitated a readjustment of traditional loyalties. Sisters and nurses were informed that 'operational management of nursing has been decentralised; all the day-to-day issues will be managed by the senior nurses in each directorate'.[36] As in other districts, nurse management was to be focused at the level of clinical activity, while a different role was developed for posts at a higher level with an emphasis on quality assurance and strategic planning. The title of the former District Nursing Officer was changed to 'Chief Nurse and Director of Quality Assurance'. Senior nurses were given dual accountability, being made managerially responsible to a Clinical Director while retaining their professional responsibility to the Chief Nurse.[37]

The arrival of clinical directorates effectively dismantled the nursing structures which had been in place since the Salmon Report and the National Health Service reorganisation of 1974. For some years there had been signs of a reaction against a system which appeared to devalue the clinical skills of nurses while promoting a management function. After the Area Health Authorities were abolished in the early 1980s the consensus principles of the previous decade fell out of favour, and the introduction of General Managers in District Authorities diminished the management role of senior nurses. In the 1970s the best salaries had been paid to nurses in administrative posts, but as the decline of the managerial function and the growth of quality assurance gave renewed significance to clinical skills ways began to be sought to improve career prospects in clinical nursing. In 1988 a new pay structure was introduced, aimed at rewarding expertise in clinical care. The establishment of directorates went a stage further in redefining the nurse's role. Following the introduction of the nursing process and the other professionalising changes which they had sought, nurses were to be full members of the clinical team, capable of making their own decisions and accepting responsibility for them, with the Sister or Charge Nurse acting as manager at ward level. At Bart's these posts were still considered to be clinical grades, but Sisters were increasingly made responsible for managing finances and other resources on their wards.[38]

All these developments closely mirrored what was happening in other parts of the National Health Service. However St Bartholomew's suffered more than most hospitals from the vagaries of government policy in the 1970s and 1980s. The measures taken by the Resource Allocation Working Party in the mid 1970s redistributed Health Service funding from London to the provinces, and within the North East Thames Region money was transferred away from centrally-located teaching hospitals. Bart's found that its resources were squeezed ever more tightly.[39] By the end of the 1980s its former independence had become a distant memory, and both policy and finance were rigidly controlled from above. Moreover, with no link between income and activity, a hospital which treated more patients was very likely to overspend its budget. In 1990 the government introduced an internal market in health services, partly in an attempt to overcome this problem but also because it believed that the old system had allowed hospitals to be inefficient and unresponsive to patients' needs. The purchasing of health care was separated from its provision; and self-governing trusts, subject to fewer bureaucratic controls, were set up within the National Health Service. Competition between providers was expected to improve efficiency. Hospitals which won contracts to treat patients would be financially rewarded while those unable to price their services competitively would be the losers. However the trusts were not to be wholly autonomous: their creation and dissolution, as well as the regulatory framework in which they operated, were to be determined by central government. A 'shadow' Trust, to manage St Bartholomew's, St Mark's, and the Hackney and Homerton Hospitals, was separated from the City and Hackney Health Authority, but permission for full trust status was refused. Central London hospitals with high costs had been expected to have difficulty competing in the market but Bart's also suffered because it was unable to collect payment for all the patients it treated.[40] The government took the view that there were too many hospitals in London and that resources should be reallocated to primary care. The Tomlinson Report of 1992 initially recommended the closure of St Bartholomew's, but in 1993 this proposal was modified in favour of a merger with the Royal London Hospital in Whitechapel. Although the merger involved rapid termination of the links between Bart's and the Homerton Hospital, the scheme went ahead and a new 'Royal Hospitals NHS Trust' was set up in April 1994, with Pamela Hibbs as its Chief Nurse. Four months later the Trust announced a plan to close the Smithfield site by the end of the century.[41]

Bart's nurses reacted to the Tomlinson Report with bewilderment and anger. To the majority it seemed scarcely possible that the Hospital might close. While most accepted that London's health care needs were changing almost all believed that St Bartholomew's should continue, and many staff and students gave vigorous support to the 'Save Bart's Campaign' organised by former patients of the Hospital. The months which followed the publication of the Report were a period of great difficulty, when nurses strove to maintain high standards of care despite low morale and continuing anxiety about the government's intentions. As the Hospital became subject to increased political controversy, a growing sense of disruption was inevitable. In October 1993 the Chief Nurse told members of the League of

Nurses that 'it seems to me that turmoil and confusion are endless'.[42] The establishment of the new Trust appeared to offer a way forward for the management of hospital services in east central London, but the future of nursing at Bart's remained uncertain.

At the time of these events the St Bartholomew's College of Nursing and Midwifery was also undergoing a significant period of change, in which it moved progressively further from its roots in the nursing service of the Hospital. In the 1980s it remained under the control of the District Health Authority, although the recruitment and assessment of students, together with virtually all responsibility for the management of teaching, were delegated to the educational staff. By the end of the decade most nursing schools had begun to develop formal links with institutions of higher education, in line with the recommendations of Project 2000. At Bart's Susan Studdy felt that the College had worked for too long in isolation from other academic disciplines and sought a closer association with City University. In 1987–8 the two institutions established a joint lectureship in psychology and after the start of Project 2000 the College began to fund further teaching posts at the University. By the beginning of the 1990s it had become clear that the introduction of the internal market would leave no place for education within the National Health Service, and that nursing schools and colleges were likely to be disengaged from health care provision and relocated in the higher education sector. In February 1991 the St Bartholomew's College of Nursing and Midwifery was formally affiliated to City University, giving staff and students access to the University's academic and social facilities as well as the opportunity to work with colleagues in other disciplines. In April of that year the Health Authority devolved the administration of the College to a newly constituted Management Board. The Principal became responsible to the Board for implementation of policy but remained managerially accountable to the Authority's Chief Nurse. Further links with City University were agreed in November 1991 when the College acquired the status of a School of Study. The Principal was coopted onto the University Senate and became an ex-officio member of its academic policy committee.[43]

These changes brought others in their wake. As the College ceased to be seen as an adjunct to the Hospital's recruitment needs, it began to adopt a terminology associated with higher education. Nursing tutors began to be called lecturers, and a board of studies was established to monitor the quality of teaching. The former distinction between clinical teachers and other tutors was abandoned, and all lecturers were expected to devote part of each week to working with students in a clinical area. At Bart's, as elsewhere, nurse education was rapidly acquiring a role and status comparable to the

*Teacher and student in an
orthopaedic ward, 1991.*

Degree course students on their graduation day, 1993.

Three nurses, 1992.

training of medical students, and the staff of the College of Nursing and Midwifery sought cooperation with colleagues at St Bartholomew's Hospital Medical College as equal partners. A Clinical Skills Centre for self-directed learning, planned as the first multi-disciplinary skills laboratory of its kind in England, was developed in the early 1990s as a joint venture between the two colleges. The Centre was completed in the autumn of 1993 and opened in May 1994.[44] Like the Medical College, the College of Nursing maintained a close connection with the Hospital and continued to use its facilities for clinical experience; but as it acquired new managerial freedoms it was also able to seek commercial sponsorship for continuing education courses and to arrange training for, and clinical placements in, a number of private hospitals.[45]

The College's relationship with the City and Hackney Health Authority was widely recognised as a provisional arrangement. The subordination of the Principal to the Chief Nurse was seen as anomalous, a relic of earlier times when the Matron had been directly responsible for training as well as nursing service. The Principal was accordingly made answerable to the Chairman of the College Management Board. At a Board meeting in August 1992 it was reported that the Regional Health Authority intended all nursing schools to be integrated into higher education within two years. The St Bartholomew's College of Nursing and Midwifery hoped to be among the first to achieve full integration, and a steering committee was established to plan the transfer of management responsibility to City University. However the publication of the Tomlinson Report in October 1992 brought a change of priorities. The Regional Health Authority proposed that the Bart's College should merge with the Princess Alexandra and Newham College which was associated with the Royal London Hospital. At a time of falling student numbers and reduced demand for qualified nurses there was general acceptance of the need for amalgamation. The proposal was agreed by the Management Boards of both Colleges in the winter of 1992–3 and was implemented with remarkable speed. The official date for the merger was set for 1 April 1993, although it was known that the new staffing structures would not be in place. The new College became known as the St Bartholomew and Princess Alexandra and Newham College of Nursing and Midwifery, and Susan Studdy became its first Principal. Its incorporation into City University was expected in 1995.[46]

REFERENCES

References beginning HA, HB, HC, MC, MO, MR, MS, SBL or X are to documentary sources in the archives of St Bartholomew's Hospital. The *League News* is the journal of the League of St Bartholomew's Nurses, also in the Hospital archives.

CHAPTER 1

1. HC2/1 fo. 7; H. Nicolas (ed.), *Proceedings and Ordinances of the Privy Council of England* (London, 1834), vol. 3, p. 131.
2. N. Moore, *The History of St Bartholomew's Hospital* (London, 1918), vol. 2, p. 754. HC2/1 fo. 7 implies that her house was on the east side of the Hospital gate, although the modern plaque is on the west side.
3. Guildhall Library, London, Ms. 9531/1 fo. 39v. Moore, *History of St Bartholomew's*, vol. 1, p. 552, refers to eight Brothers but in the manuscript at Guildhall Library the figure is seven.
4. HC3 mem. 14; Guildhall Library, Mss. 9531/1 fo. 39v., 25121/643, 25121/644, 25121/647; *Valor Ecclesiasticus* (Record Commission, London, 1810), vol. 1, p. 389.
5. HC1/38.
6. HC1/1142; Moore, *History of St Bartholomew's*, vol. 1, pp. 137–9.
7. HC1/734; HC1/1179.
8. HC2/1 fo. 8.
9. HC2/1 fo. 597; Moore, *History of St Bartholomew's*, vol. 1, pp. 471–2.

CHAPTER 2

1. HC1/2001; HC3 mem. 17.
2. Greater London Record Office, H1/ST/E14 pp. 113, 122.
3. HC3 mem. 14–15; *The Ordre of the Hospital of S. Bartholomewes in Westsmythfielde in London* (London, 1552), charge to Matron.
4. SBL10/1, October 1547; HA1/1 *passim*.
5. HA1/1 fo. 6r.; *Ordre of the Hospital*, charges to Matron and Sisters.
6. HA1/1 fo. 203r.; E. M. McInnes, *St Thomas' Hospital* (London, 1963), p. 27.
7. HA1/1 ff. 1r., 118r.; HB1/1 fo. 107r.; N. J. M. Kerling, 'The First Blue Uniform', *St Bartholomew's Hospital Journal* March 1963, p. 47.
8. HB12/2 ff. 157–89; *Ordre of the Hospital*, charge to Matron. Separate wards for male and female patients are mentioned in 1546: HC3 mem. 17.
9. *Ordre of the Hospital*, charge to Matron; HA1/1 ff. 5r., 181v., 191r.
10. HA1/5 fo. 89r.; HA1/7 fo. 52r.
11. HA1/1 ff. 6r., 79r.; HA1/5 ff. 20r., 224v.; HA1/7 fo. 17v.
12. HA1/1 ff. 69v., 77v.; HA1/3 fo. 238v.; HA1/5 fo. 37r.; HA1/8 fo. 163r./190r.; HA4 fo. 38r.

13. HA1/2 fo. 260r.; HA1/7 ff. 41v., 192r.; HA1/8 fo. 156v./183v.; HA4 fo. 38v.
14. HA1/5 ff. 15–16; HA4 fo. 38v.; HA1/12 pp. 458–60.
15. HA1/5 fo. 287v.
16. HA4 fo. 24v.
17. HA1/5 ff. 5–6, 56r., 77–8; HB1/6. At Christ's Hospital the women who cared for the children in the wards were called 'nurses' in 1557, almost a century before the word came into use at St Bartholomew's: cf. *The Order of the Hospitals of K. Henry the VIIIth and K. Edward the VIth* (London, 1557).
18. N. J. M. Kerling, 'Nursing in St Bartholomew's Hospital in the 17th Century', *St Bartholomew's Hospital Journal* August 1970, at p. 279.
19. HA1/4 fo. 336.
20. HA1/9 fo. 50r.
21. N. J. M. Kerling, 'A Seventeenth Century Hospital Matron, Margaret Blague', *Transactions of the London and Middlesex Archaeological Society* 1970, pp. 30–6.
22. HA1/1 ff. 11r., 191r.; HB1/1 fo. 51v.
23. HB1/7 *passim*; HA1/5 fo. 9r.; HA4 fo. 21r.
24. HA1/1 fo. 171r.; HA1/4 fo. 274r.; HA1/8 fo. 281r./309r.; HA1/9 fo. 185r.; HA4 fo. 60r.; D. Power, 'The Hospital Beer', *St Bartholomew's Hospital Journal* September 1938, p. 298.
25. HA1/4 fo. 321v.; Moore, *History of St Bartholomew's*, vol. 2, pp. 762–4; Kerling, 'Nursing in the 17th Century', at p. 279.
26. HA1/5 ff. 44v., 173v., 255v.; HA 1/7 ff. 121r., 134v.; HA1/8 ff. 51r./77r., 133r./159r. Such behaviour was probably not new: similar problems occurred at St Thomas' Hospital in the sixteenth century (cf. C. T. Daly, 'The Hospitals of London: administration, refoundation and benefaction c.1500–1572', Oxford D. Phil. thesis, 1993, pp. 292–5); and at St Bartholomew's the detailed rules in the *Ordre of the Hospital* of 1552, especially those relating to drunkenness and nocturnal visits to the wards, perhaps imply that some Sisters had already transgressed in these areas of conduct.
27. HA1/5 ff. 153v., 186r.; HA1/8 fo. 19v./45v.; HA4 fo. 46v.
28. HA1/5 fo. 20r.; HA1/8 fo. 24r./50r.; HA1/9 ff. 49–50.
29. HA1/1 fo. 183r.; HA1/3 ff. 137r., 178r.; HA1/4 fo. 134r.; HA1/8 fo. 7v./33v.; HA4 ff. 4r., 34v.
30. HA1/4 fo. 236v.; HA1/5 fo. 56; HA1/9 fo. 7v.; HA4 fo. 34v.
31. HA1/7 fo. 335r.; HA1/10 fo. 40v.; Kerling, 'Nursing in the 17th Century', at p. 279. The Sister's name is variously recorded as Dynne, Dyne, Dynn and Ginn; Moore, *History of St Bartholomew's*, vol. 2, p. 765, gives it as 'Pyne'.
32. HA1/8 ff. 37r./63r., 72v./98v.; HA4 fo. 27.
33. HA1/1 fo. 27r.; cf. HA1/3 fo. 261v., HA1/8 fo. 142v./168v., HA4 fo. 21r.
34. *Ordre of the Hospital*, charge to Sisters; HB1/1 fo. 108v.; HA1/2 fo. 34v.; HA1/8 fo. 239r./266r.
35. D. Power, 'The Rebuilding of the Hospital in the Eighteenth Century', *St Bartholomew's Hospital Reports* 1926, pp. 9–34, and 1927, pp. 7–24; HA1/12 pp. 157, 430; Gibbs's plan of 1729, reproduced in G. Whitteridge and V. Stokes, *A Brief History of the Hospital of St Bartholomew* (London, 1961), p. 34. Moore, *History of St Bartholomew's*, vol. 2, p. 769, dates the introduction of separate rooms to 1787, misinterpreting an entry in HA1/15 p. 57.
36. HA1/4 ff. 296r., 314v.; HB13/1–2.

37. HA1/11 p. 431; HA1/12 p. 508.

38. HA1/14 pp. 70–2.

39. HA1/16 pp. 74–7.

40. The earliest, reproduced on p. 16, shows Rahere Ward in 1832 or 1833. It was published in *British Medical Journal* 19 June 1897, where the original water-colour sketch is said to have hung in the ward. It was again reproduced in D. Power, *A Short History of St Bartholomew's Hospital* (London, 1923), plate XXVIII. The original has since been lost.

41. HA1/16 p. 558; HA1/17 pp. 18, 324; J. Paget, *St Bartholomew's Hospital and School Fifty Years Ago* (London, 1885), p. 8; *League News* 1902 p. 136; W. Church, 'St Bartholomew's Hospital and Medicine during the last Fifty Years', *St Bartholomew's Hospital Journal* July 1912, at p. 176; N. J. M. Kerling, 'In Olden Times', *St Bartholomew's Hospital Journal* May 1969, pp. 190–1; G. Yeo, *Images of Bart's: an illustrated history of St Bartholomew's Hospital* (London, 1992), p. 94.

42. *Rules and Orders for the Government of St Bartholomew's Hospital* (London, 1814), pp. 77–94; *32nd Report of the Commissioners . . . to continue the Inquiries concerning Charities in England and Wales*, part VI (London, 1840), p. 54.

43. 'Twenty-four Hours in a London Hospital', *St Bartholomew's Hospital Reports* 1924, at pp. 7–8; G. Yeo, *Ward Names at Bart's* (London, 1990). The practice seems to have originated in the seventeenth century, the first known example being the burial of Sarah Smith, 'Sister Queen', at St Bartholomew the Less in August 1662: SBL10/2. Further early instances are in HA4 fo. 34v. and HA 1/7 ff. 78, 328; but other usages (e.g. 'Sister of Queen Ward') were not wholly superseded until the nineteenth century.

44. HA1/5 fo. 87r.; HA1/8 fo. 176r./203r.; HA1/12 p. 573; *Rules and Orders* (1814), pp. 82–3, 89. The night rail formed part of the Sisters' uniform from 1687 to 1843; it was also worn on the annual View Day and Sisters who died in office were buried in their night rails: HA1/7 fo. 191v.; HA1/19 p. 180; Moore, *History of St Bartholomew's*, vol. 2, p. 771.

45. C. Dickens, *Martin Chuzzlewit*, chapters 19, 25; preface to edition of 1849/50.

46. A. Willett, 'The Surgical Side of the Hospital Fifty Years Ago', *St Bartholomew's Hospital Journal* October 1910, at p. 5; *32nd Report of the Commissioners concerning Charities*, p. 54; Paget, *St Bartholomew's Hospital and School Fifty Years Ago*, pp. 26–7.

47. HA1/14 pp. 277, 562; further evidence from the 1770s and later is discussed by C. Helmstadter, 'Old Nurses and New', *Nursing History Review* 1993, at p. 47.

48. H. Marsh, 'Some Former Acquaintances', *St Bartholomew's Hospital Journal* February 1904, at p. 87.

49. HA1/15 *passim*.

50. *Rules and Orders for the Government of St Bartholomew's Hospital* (London, 1833), p. 34.

51. HA3/5 pp. 14, 17; Paget, *St Bartholomew's Hospital and School Fifty Years Ago*, p. 26.

52. *32nd Report of the Commissioners concerning Charities*, p. 54.

53. Paget, *St Bartholomew's Hospital and School Fifty Years Ago*, p. 26; HA1/17 pp. 189, 194; HA3/2 pp. 131, 145; HA3/3 p. 259.

54. HA3/2 pp. 59, 131, 219; HA3/7 pp. 41–2, 140; HA1/21 p. 532.

55. HA1/20 pp. 166–73.

56. 'Twenty-four Hours in a London Hospital', at p. 8; Willett, 'Surgical Side of the Hospital', at p. 5.

57. S. A. Tooley, *The History of Nursing in the British Empire* (London, 1906), p. 134.

58. Church, 'St Bartholomew's Hospital and Medicine', at p. 176; D. Duckworth,

Sick Nursing: essentially a woman's mission (London, 1877), pp. 10, 23, reprinted in D. Duckworth, *Views on some Social Subjects* (London, 1915), pp. 201, 214.

59. HA1/16 pp. 76, 560; HA1/17 pp. 323–6.

60. HA1/22 p. 264; HA1/24 p. 121; *British Medical Journal* 28 February 1874.

61. *32nd Report of the Commissioners concerning Charities*, p. 54; HA1/18 p. 497. The Sisters' Sunday food ration was replaced by a cash payment in 1870: HA1/23 p. 346.

62. Greater London Record Office, A/NFC/22/4 p. 53; Tooley, *History of Nursing*, p. 135; *The Lancet* 18 December 1869; *British Medical Journal* 28 February 1874.

63. HC1/2001; Kerling, 'Nursing in the 17th Century', at p. 278.

64. HB13/1. The figure of 280 beds is inferred from HA1/9 ff. 148r., 150r., where the addition of 70 new beds is said to represent an increase of one third over the previous figure.

65. HA1/17 pp. 178, 324–5, 367; HA1/20 p. 552; *32nd Report of the Commissioners concerning Charities*, p. 56.

66. *Pall Mall Gazette* 22 November 1869.

67. *32nd Report of the Commissioners concerning Charities*, p. 54.

68. A. Willett, 'A Historical Review of Changes in Procedure', *St Bartholomew's Hospital Journal* October 1901, at p. 5.

69. *The Times* 27 October 1869; *The Lancet* 20 November 1869, 18 December 1869; *Pall Mall Gazette* 22 November 1869; *British Medical Journal* 28 February 1874; Tooley, *History of Nursing*, pp. 135–6.

70. *32nd Report of the Commissioners concerning Charities*, pp. 58, 63; *The Lancet* 2 October 1869, 20 November 1869, 18 December 1869, 15 January 1870; *The Times* 27 October 1869; *Pall Mall Gazette* 22 November 1869; *Daily News* 27 November 1869; J. A. Ormerod, 'The History of our Special Departments', *St Bartholomew's Hospital Journal* August 1901, at p. 163; Church, 'St Bartholomew's Hospital and Medicine', at p. 174.

CHAPTER 3

1. X102.

2. HA1/23 pp. 207–8; Greater London Record Office, A/NFC/22/4 pp. 51–2; Tooley, *History of Nursing*, pp. 134–5. The Governors' confidence was perhaps misplaced. Not only did the nurses still have to fetch and carry most of the ward supplies, but one Sister felt that the scrubbers' twice-weekly cleaning of her ward floor was insufficient and made her nurses repeat the exercise on two further days each week: Greater London Record Office, A/NFC/22/4 p. 52.

3. HA1/23 pp. 398–403; *British Medical Journal* 28 February 1874.

4. Greater London Record Office, H1/ST/NC15/13, A/NFC/22/4 pp. 5–6, 14–15; cf. R. White, *Social Change and the Development of the Nursing Profession* (London, 1978), p. 51.

5. G. Smalley, *The Life of Sir Sydney H. Waterlow, Bart.* (London, 1909), pp. 171, 177–8.

6. HA1/24 pp. 314–19; HA3/12 p. 213; X5/26 p. 5.

7. *League News* 1902 p. 134; Church, 'St Bartholomew's Hospital and Medicine', at p. 176; Duckworth, *Sick Nursing*, p. 21.

8. HA1/24 pp. 314–19; HA3/12 pp. 225–6. The title of 'ward maid' was usual in other

hospitals and by the end of the nineteenth century had displaced the term 'ward assistant' at Bart's.

9. MO1/1, 16 December 1880; HA1/26 p. 529; *League News* 1902 p. 137.

10. HA1/24 pp. 314–19; HA3/12 pp. 225–6; *League News* 1902 pp. 136–7.

11. HA1/22 p. 475; Smalley, *Life of Waterlow*, p. 171.

12. Tooley, *History of Nursing*, p. 136.

13. *Pall Mall Gazette* 22 November 1869; *The Lancet* 15 January 1870; *League News* 1902 p. 134.

14. MO53/1 pp. 1-2; *League News* 1902 p. 134.

15. Duckworth, *Sick Nursing*, pp. 14–25. In the same month Maria Machin, who later became Matron, wrote to Florence Nightingale from Canada that the opening of a training school at St Bartholomew's provided further evidence of the success of her nursing movement: British Library, Ms. Add. 47745 fo. 81.

16. *League News* 1902 p. 134.

17. HA3/12 p. 214; MC1/1 pp. 317–18.

18. *League News* 1902 pp. 134–8.

19. *League News* 1902 p. 137, 1903 p. 180; Willett, 'Historical Review of Changes in Procedure', at p. 6; Willett, 'Surgical Side of the Hospital', at p. 4; T. H. Pennington, 'Listerism, its Decline and its Persistence', *Medical History* 1995, at p. 50.

20. MO53/1 pp. 1–2; HA3/13 p. 52; *League News* 1902 pp. 137–8.

21. HA1/24 p. 549; *Report from the Select Committee on Metropolitan Hospitals* (London, 1890), p. 167.

22. British Library, Ms. Add. 47745 fo. 109; Greater London Record Office, H1/ST/NC1/78/1, H1/ST/NC18/13/11; Smalley, *Life of Waterlow*, p. 178.

23. Greater London Record Office, H1/ST/NTS/C1/2 p. 18, H1/ST/NTS/C4/2 p. 65, H1/ST/NTS/C7/2.

24. British Library, Ms. Add. 47745 ff. 91–5; Greater London Record Office, H1/ST/NC15/34, H1/ST/NC18/13/32–46.

25. British Library, Ms. Add. 47719 fo. 197.

26. British Library, Ms. Add. 47745 ff. 80–1, 87. A year earlier she had written that 'I am beginning to think that the range of my superintending duties is too extensive for me': ibid., fo. 66.

27. British Library, Ms. Add. 47745 ff. 109, 120–3; Greater London Record Office, H1/ST/NC1/78/1, H1/ST/NC18/13/11; W. E. Hector, *The Work of Mrs Bedford Fenwick and the Rise of Professional Nursing* (London, 1973), p. 25.

28. Greater London Record Office, H1/ST/NC18/13/76–7, H1/ST/NC1/78/7, H1/ST/NTS/A3/3/1.

29. HA3/13 pp. 233–4.

30. British Library, Mss. Add. 47745 fo. 138, Add. 45808 ff. 14–15.

31. HA1/25 p. 180; Greater London Record Office, H1/ST/NC18/13/78; British Library, Ms. Add. 47745 ff. 133–4.

32. Hector, *Mrs Bedford Fenwick*, pp. 1–2.

33. HA1/25 p. 244; *League News* 1950 p. 12; Smalley, *Life of Waterlow*, pp. 179–80.

34. *League News* 1950 p. 12.

35. *Report from the Committee on Metropolitan Hospitals* (1890), p. 546.

36. HA3/14 p. 216; HA3/15 p. 331; MO54/1; *League News* 1902 p. 137.

37. *Report from the Committee on Metropolitan Hospitals* (1890), p. 549.

38. *League News* 1902 p. 138, 1950 pp. 14–15.

39. MO53/1 p. 17 and *passim*.

40. *League News* 1902 p. 135; Greater London Record Office, A/NFC/22/4 p. 51.

41. HA3/14 p. 88; H. Morten, *How to Become a Nurse* (London, 1893), pp. 156–7; Hector, *Mrs Bedford Fenwick*, p. 29. A photograph of the Matron and Sisters in the 1880s (X8/957; reproduced here on p. 39) shows every Sister dressed in the uniform which Manson designed.

42. HA3/14 p. 88; *League News* 1902 p. 138; Morten, *How to Become a Nurse*, pp. 156–7; D. Power, 'Famous Hospitals and Medical Schools', *The Practitioner* January 1905, at p. 120. By the beginning of the twentieth century Sisters, like staff nurses, wore blue belts with ornate buckles, but in earlier photographs Sisters are seen wearing plain white belts.

43. MO53/1 pp. 12–14; MO54/1 pp. 1–26.

44. HA1/25 p. 444; *2nd Report from the Select Committee on Metropolitan Hospitals* (London, 1891), p. 48. They were known elsewhere as 'lady pupils' or 'paying probationers'.

45. Paget, *St Bartholomew's Hospital and School Fifty Years Ago*, p. 27; *Report from the Committee on Metropolitan Hospitals* (1890), p. 165; *3rd Report from the Committee on Metropolitan Hospitals* (1892), p. 27; HA3/15 pp. 150–1.

46. *Report from the Committee on Metropolitan Hospitals* (1890), pp. 165–7. In 1891 the Clerk to the Governors reported that 'the class of people we have engaged in nursing has very much altered within the last ten or a dozen years' and that all the Sisters and at least five-sixths of the nurses were by then 'what are commonly described as ladies': *2nd Report from the Committee on Metropolitan Hospitals* (1891), p. 48. For the social background of Bart's nurses at this time see also A. Simnett, 'The Pursuit of Respectability', in R. White (ed.), *Political Issues in Nursing: past, present and future*, vol. 2 (Chichester, 1986), pp. 1–23.

47. HA1/26 pp. 16–17; *League News* 1926 pp. 11–12, 1948 p. 15.

48. *Report from the Committee on Metropolitan Hospitals* (1890), p. 548.

49. For her subsequent career see Hector, *Mrs Bedford Fenwick*, and S. McGann, *The Battle of the Nurses* (London, 1992), chapter 2. Her maiden name was Ethel Gordon Manson and on marriage she became Ethel Gordon Fenwick, but following the fashion of the time she chose to be known publicly by her husband's name: as Dr Bedford Fenwick's wife she was known as Mrs Bedford Fenwick.

50. *League News* 1908 pp. 358–9, 1912 pp. 255–6.

51. HA3/20 pp. 192–3; MO29/1.

52. *2nd Report from the Committee on Metropolitan Hospitals* (1891), pp. 46–8; *3rd Report from the Committee on Metropolitan Hospitals* (1892), pp. clxviii, 27; *League News* 1908 p. 360.

53. I. Stewart, 'A Practical View of Nursing', *Murray's Magazine* August 1890, at pp. 165, 167.

54. X5/25 p. 2; Marsh, 'Some Former Acquaintances', at p. 87; D. Power, 'The School Prize Medals', *St Bartholomew's Hospital Journal* August 1911, at p. 169.

55. 'Notes', *St Bartholomew's Hospital Journal* April 1895, at p. 106.

56. HA3/20 pp. 17, 193.

57. HA3/25 pp. 309, 318; HA3/27 pp. 27, 301–3; *League News* 1907 p. 227, 1950 p. 14.

58. *League News* 1907 p. 277.

59. HA3/30 p. 24.

60. *League News* 1910 p. 134. Recruitment practices in the 1880s can be gauged from the photograph reproduced on p. 39, in which several Sisters are wearing the badge of the Nightingale School.

61. MO54/1 p. 59. Simnett, 'Pursuit of Respectability', p. 6, points out that a number of women used their training as a means to social advancement and that several Bart's nurses of working-class origin became superintendents at provincial hospitals.

62. MO54/2 pp. 18, 21; M. B. Byrnes, *Celebrating 100 Years of Excellence in Nursing Education* (Philadelphia, 1987), pp. 17–23.

63. A. F. Bradshaw, *Catharine Grace Loch: a memoir* (London, 1905); MO54/1 pp. 142, 149, 162, 170, 173.

64. *League News* 1910 p. 126, 1911 p. 171; MO53/1 pp. 10, 20, 38. Mabel Sleigh's notebooks from her time as a probationer are held in the Hospital archives (X103).

65. 'Dinner to Mr Willett', *St Bartholomew's Hospital Journal* October 1902, at pp. 15–16; Stewart, 'Practical View of Nursing', at p. 169.

66. HA1/24 p. 121; MO51; HA3/18 p. 237; HA3/20 p. 2; HA3/22 p. 120; HA3/40 p. 123; *3rd Report from the Committee on Metropolitan Hospitals* (1892), p. 27.

67. *League News* 1902 p. 137, 1907 p. 227.

68. After the introduction of the compulsory fourth year of service the number of probationers as a proportion of the total workforce fell slightly, from 74% in 1890 to 68% in 1908 (calculated from figures in *Report from the Committee on Metropolitan Hospitals* (1890), p. 165, and MS90).

69. HA3/17 p. 268; HA3/29 p. 190; HA3/31 p. 50; *League News* 1907 p. 227.

70. MS90; *3rd Report from the Committee on Metropolitan Hospitals* (1892), p. 27; G. Bourne, *We Met at Bart's* (London, 1963), p. 54.

71. HA1/26 pp. 324–5; *League News* 1908 p. 360. In the 1830s one Sister was allocated to casualty duties (*32nd Report of the Commissioners concerning Charities*, p. 54), but she received lower pay than the other Sisters and was also referred to as the 'casualty-nurse'. The increase in staff at the end of the century was a response to growth in patient numbers: cf. Yeo, *Images of Bart's*, pp. 115, 117.

72. Willett, 'Surgical Side of the Hospital', at p. 5; HA3/27 p. 241; *League News* 1908 p. 360, 1911 p. 212.

73. Stewart, 'Practical View of Nursing', at pp. 162–3, 168.

74. *British Journal of Nursing* December 1927.

75. *Nursing Record* 19 May 1894, 14 July 1894; D. C. Bridges, *A History of the International Council of Nurses* (London, 1967), p. 8. The Matron's house at that time was on the site later occupied by the Isla Stewart Memorial Library, and not in Little Britain as stated in the account of this episode in V. C. Medvei and J. L. Thornton (eds.), *The Royal Hospital of St Bartholomew 1123–1973* (London, 1974), p. 253.

76. MO38/2; *British Journal of Nursing* December 1927.

77. *League News* 1907 pp. 272–7; D. Power, 'In Memoriam of Miss Isla Stewart', *St Bartholomew's Hospital Journal* April 1910, at p. 108; *British Journal of Nursing* 2 December 1911.

78. *League News* 1900 pp. 1–3, 1905 p. 116, 1941 p. 33; McGann, *Battle of the Nurses*, pp. 67–8; Hector, *Mrs Bedford Fenwick*, pp. 22, 35.

79. *League News* 1905 p. 78, 1910 p. 135.

80. *British Journal of Nursing* 19 March 1910.

81. *League News* 1910 p. 135, 1912 p. 257.

CHAPTER 4

1. *The Lancet* 18 June 1910; *League News* 1910 pp. 134–6; L. L. Dock, *A History of Nursing* (New York, 1912), vol. 3, p. 53; McGann, *Battle of the Nurses*, p. 77.

2. HA3/34 pp. 207, 247; HA1/29 pp. 77–9.

3. McGann, *Battle of the Nurses*, pp. 30–1, 201.

4. *League News* 1916 p. 697, 1917 p. 782, 1919 p. 161, 1925 p. 14.

5. Yeo, *Images of Bart's*, pp. 108–9; *League News* 1911 pp. 172, 214, 1934 p. 9; MO38/1; MO38/4; MO38/28; HA3/44 pp. 71–2.

6. MO38/6/1; MO38/13/1; HA3/39 p. 275; MO57/2.

7. *League News* 1915 pp. 542–53; V. Brittain, *Testament of Youth* (London, 1933), pp. 206, 309.

8. E. Wilson, *Gone with the Raj* (Wymondham, Norfolk, 1974), p. 6.

9. Hector, *Mrs Bedford Fenwick*, p. 45.

10. P. Allan and M. Jolley, *Nursing, Midwifery and Health Visiting since 1900* (London, 1982), p. 42.

11. HA3/44 p. 52. Until 1950 even the first-year examinations were duplicated: MO23/1 p. 6.

12. *League News* 1922 p. 131, 1925 p. 1.

13. MO38/21/2; MO38/34/1.

14. MO53/2; HA3/39 p. 92; HA3/42 p. 204.

15. *League News* 1980 pp. 27–8; Wilson, *Gone with the Raj*, p. 6.

16. MO38/6/1; *League News* 1925 p. 25, 1980 p. 27.

17. HA3/27 pp. 27, 301–3; MO38/6; MO38/17.

18. MO31; *League News* 1925 pp. 21–2, 1988 p. 14; W. E. Hector, unpublished autobiography (typescript, 1989), p. 55.

19. MO33/5; MO44/4; *League News* 1988 pp. 32–3, 1992 p. 36; further information supplied by Elsie Hall and Evelyn Swabey.

20. *League News* 1968 pp. 29–31, 1980 pp. 28–9, 1988 p. 33; MO38/27/1; Wilson, *Gone with the Raj*, pp. 6–8; further information supplied by Elsie Hall and Evelyn Swabey.

21. MO33/5; MO44/4; *League News* 1980 p. 29, 1988 p. 33; Bourne, *We Met at Bart's*, p. 54; further information supplied by Elsie Hall and Evelyn Swabey.

22. *League News* 1980 p. 29; further information supplied by Elsie Hall and Evelyn Swabey.

23. Medvei and Thornton (eds.), *The Royal Hospital of St Bartholomew*, p. 256; Hector, autobiography, p. 64; further information supplied by Evelyn Swabey.

24. MO34/2; MO38/17; MO38/26/3; *League News* 1952 p. 38.

25. *St Bartholomew's Hospital Treasurer's Report* 1925 p. 32; *League News* 1932 pp. 9–13, 1952 p. 38, 1980 p. 29.

26. MO38/18/3–4; MO44/4–5; *League News* 1934 p. 11, 1969 p. 10; further information supplied by Elsie Hall and Evelyn Swabey.

27. MO44/4–5; W. E. Hector, 'Coronation Thoughts on Nursing', *St Bartholomew's Hospital Journal* June 1953, at p. 138.

28. MO33/1; MO33/4; MO33/6; *League News* 1980 p. 28, 1988 p. 32; further information supplied by Evelyn Swabey.

29. *League News* 1926 p. 6, 1980 p. 28. The last 'frilly' cap did not retire until the 1950s: J. Foster, 'Nurses' Uniforms Through the Ages', *Bart's Journal* Summer 1983, at p. 28.

30. Cf. photograph reproduced on p. 48.

31. Hector, autobiography, p. 63; *League News* 1992 p. 36; further information supplied by Elsie Hall and Evelyn Swabey.
32. St Bartholomew's Hospital, Charge to Sisters, 1936; *League News* 1980 p. 29; Hector, autobiography, p. 60; further information supplied by Elsie Hall and Evelyn Swabey.
33. Medvei and Thornton (eds.), *The Royal Hospital of St Bartholomew*, p. 255.
34. In 1927 when Mrs Bedford Fenwick sought permission to address the staff about her project for a British College of Nurses, McIntosh sent a formal letter of refusal: MO38/38.
35. *League News* 1927 pp. 1, 5–6.
36. MO32/2 p. 6; Hector, autobiography, pp. 51, 58; Hector, 'Coronation Thoughts', at p. 137; Medvei and Thornton (eds.), *The Royal Hospital of St Bartholomew*, p. 255; *League News* 1980 p. 30.
37. *League News* 1968 pp. 1–2.
38. MO10; MO15; MO20; MO38.
39. Information supplied by Elsie Hall.
40. Information supplied by Winifred Hector and Elsie Hall.
41. MO40/4–6; *League News* 1934 p. 8; B. Abel-Smith, *A History of the Nursing Profession* (London, 1960), p. 135; further information supplied by Elsie Hall. The Sister in charge of the Special Treatment Centre (for venereal diseases) was the only Sister who lived out and was paid £225 per annum: MO40/5.
42. *League News* 1934 p. 8.
43. *2nd Report from the Committee on Metropolitan Hospitals* (1891), pp. 151, 158.
44. Yeo, *Images of Bart's*, p. 52.
45. T. A. Lodge, 'The New Surgical and Operation Blocks', *St Bartholomew's Hospital Reports* 1930, at p. 22; Yeo, *Images of Bart's*, pp. 48–50, 53; *League News* 1980 pp. 27–8.
46. *League News* 1934 p. 9; MO32/1.
47. W. P. S. Branson, 'Observations on the Health of a Nursing Staff', *St Bartholomew's Hospital Reports* 1933, pp. 125–38; Hector, autobiography, p. 57; Hector, 'Coronation Thoughts', at p. 136; Medvei and Thornton (eds.), *The Royal Hospital of St Bartholomew*, p. 255.
48. *League News* 1934 p. 13; MO39/11.
49. The pink uniform was in occasional use for 'temporary Sisters' or 'nurses doing Sisters' duties' in 1899 (MO5/1 p. 47; *League News* 1900 p. 29, 1901 p. 55) but does not seem to have been widely employed until Helen Dey's time.
50. *League News* 1934 p. 11; MO33/5; MO39/11.
51. MO24/12.
52. *St Bartholomew's Hospital Treasurer's Report* 1929 p. 50; MO39/11.
53. Hector, 'Coronation Thoughts', at p. 138; MO32/3 p. 14; *League News* 1934 pp. 12–13.
54. *St Bartholomew's Hospital Treasurer's Report* 1939 pp. 33–7.
55. Medvei and Thornton (eds.), *The Royal Hospital of St Bartholomew*, pp. 256–7, 259; *League News* 1993 p. 19; *St Bartholomew's Hospital Treasurer's Report* 1940 pp. 29–32.
56. Medvei and Thornton (eds.), *The Royal Hospital of St Bartholomew*, p. 257; further information supplied by Winifred Hector and Pat Haworth.
57. MO40/11; Abel-Smith, *History of the Nursing Profession*, p. 121. The number of enquiries fell from 2119 in 1932 to 1323 in 1938, but even the latter figure represented almost nine enquiries for every place: *St Bartholomew's Hospital Treasurer's Report* 1938 p. 39.
58. *League News* 1944 p. 6, 1950 p. 5, 1987 p. 23. For a number of years a striped belt was

the mark of a first-year nurse, but it was later reallocated to second-years and the first-years wore grey belts.

59. Hector, autobiography, p. 89.

60. Hector, autobiography, pp. 59, 90; further information supplied by Winifred Hector.

61. Medvei and Thornton (eds.), *The Royal Hospital of St Bartholomew*, p. 255; Hector, *Mrs Bedford Fenwick*, p. 6; Yeo, *Ward Names at Bart's*, p. 4. Bedford Fenwick Ward was the first in the Hospital to be named after a nurse. The author was present at the meeting when this name was decided on. Many of the medical staff had never heard of Mrs Bedford Fenwick and at least one distinguished consultant was very distressed at what he perceived as a break with tradition in naming a ward after someone who was not a doctor. Many nurses, however, were delighted that one of their number should at last be honoured in this way.

CHAPTER 5

1. HA3/59 pp. 97, 258.

2. MO23/1 p. 35.

3. Hector, 'Coronation Thoughts', at pp. 138–9.

4. MO30/3/1.

5. MO24/2/5.

6. MO23/1 pp. 3, 5, 9; MO24/4.

7. MO24/6.

8. MO24/5.

9. MO23/1 p. 18; MO24/8.

10. MO23/1 pp. 5–6; MO24/4; MO24/6; further information supplied by Sybil Allen and Mary Walker.

11. MO23/1 pp. 13, 15; MO24/6; Hector, 'Coronation Thoughts', at p. 138.

12. MO23/1 pp. 25–6; *League News* 1954 p. 20.

13. Medvei and Thornton (eds.), *The Royal Hospital of St Bartholomew*, p. 259; Hector, autobiography, p. 129; further information supplied by Winifred Hector. There were also continuing difficulties in providing balanced ward experience for students, as the Hospital had more surgical than medical wards and the two children's wards were insufficient to provide adequate paediatric experience: MO23/1 pp. 15, 30; MO24/11/11; MO24/32/4–5.

14. *League News* 1969 p. 10, 1980 p. 29; further information supplied by Elsie Hall.

15. B. Cantrell, 'Training to be a Nurse: has anything changed?', *Barts Journal* Spring 1992, p. 29.

16. Information supplied by Sybil Allen and Mary Walker.

17. *Report of the Working Party on the Recruitment and Training of Nurses* (London, 1947), p. 69.

18. MO24/11/4–5; *League News* 1962 p. 5.

19. MO40/5; MO40/8; *League News* 1934 p. 13.

20. Medvei and Thornton (eds.), *The Royal Hospital of St Bartholomew*, p. 256; MO23/1 p. 22.

21. Yeo, *Images of Bart's*, p. 46.

22. MO24/11/2–3; *St Bartholomew's Hospital Treasurer's Report* 1938 pp. 40–1.

23. MO23/2 pp. 105–6.

24. MO24/11/2–3; MO23/2 pp. 105–6.

25. W. A. Guttridge, 'The New Surgical In-patients Block in Little Britain', *St Bartholomew's Hospital Journal* October 1957, at p. 315.

26. Information supplied by Elsie Hall, Sybil Allen and Mary Walker.

27. *League News* 1960 p. 48.

28. *League News* 1962 pp. 9–10.

29. MO24/11/13–14; *League News* 1962 p. 5; further information supplied by Sybil Allen, Mary Walker and Winifred Hector.

30. MO24/11/13; MO24/14/1; *League News* 1962 p. 5, 1966 p. 44; further information supplied by Winifred Hector and Carol Bavin.

31. *League News* 1964 pp. 14–15, 1966 p. 24.

32. MO24/14/4.

33. MO23/2 pp. 19–20; *League News* 1968 p. 32, 1970 p. 15.

34. MO24/16/1; Hector, autobiography, pp. 192–3.

35. MO24/16/12; Medvei and Thornton (eds.), *The Royal Hospital of St Bartholomew*, pp. 259–60.

36. *League News* 1967 p. 3; Medvei and Thornton (eds.), *The Royal Hospital of St Bartholomew*, p. 260.

37. *League News* 1966 p. 23; MO24/26/3.

38. MO24/29/6; MO24/37/1.

39. MO23/2 pp. 112–18, 123, 138; R. Aspdin, 'Nurses Report', *St Bartholomew's Hospital Journal* September 1970, p. 297; further information supplied by Elsie Hall, Sybil Allen and Mary Walker.

40. *Report of the Committee on Senior Nursing Staff Structure* (London, 1966), pp. 6, 26.

41. MO24/17/5; MO24/21/12.

42. MO24/17/15; MO24/25/1–2; further information supplied by Elsie Hall, Sybil Allen, Mary Walker and Winifred Hector.

43. MO24/17/9; MO24/37/1; further information supplied by Sybil Allen and Mary Walker.

44. MO24/25/3.

45. MO67/1; *League News* 1950 p. 5.

46. J. A. Ingram, 'Bart's Nurses 1123–1973', in *Bart's 850 Years* (St Bartholomew's Hospital, London, 1973), p. 16.

47. *League News* 1967 pp. 36–8, 1973 pp. 13–17.

48. MO23/2 p. 129; *League News* 1970 p. 5. The rule against marriage had ceased to be strictly enforced in the nineteenth century: Marion Mallard, a nurse in Luke Ward in 1871, was the wife of a soldier in the Coldstream Guards (SBL10/7 p. 50; MR5/12, 21 November 1871). However there remained a strong presumption against it: in the early twentieth century nurses believed that they could not retain their jobs if they married (*League News* 1992 p. 37) and the Hospital accepted only single women or widows for training (MO30/3/1). The national campaign to recruit married women started in 1961.

49. MO24/36/3; MO24/37/1.

50. MO24/24.

51. *League News* 1967 p. 31, 1970 p. 15.

52. MO23/2 p. 53.

53. *League News* 1967 p. 32; MO24/32/6.

54. *League News* 1968 p. 2.

55. MO24/11/3; MO24/32/3; *League News* 1967 p. 10, 1970 p. 17; *Report of the Committee on Nursing* (London, 1972), p. 116.

56. MO23/2 p. 46; MO24/32/3; MO24/34; MO24/35.
57. MO24/24/1; MO24/36/3; *League News* 1971 p. 11, 1973 p. 20, 1987 p. 24; further information supplied by Carol Bavin.
58. Information supplied by Carol Bavin.
59. *League News* 1970 p. 15, 1971 p. 11.
60. MO24/32/3; MO24/32/5. Secondments began in the 1950s when small numbers of student nurses were able to spend two months on psychiatric work at Hill End. After 1962 there was a choice of obstetric or psychiatric nursing but places were in short supply (*League News* 1969 p. 13) and until the start of the 1970s the School could not offer a secondment to every student.
61. MO24/11/6–7; MO24/11/12–13; MO24/32/4; MO24/32/7.
62. *St Bartholomew's Hospital Treasurer's Report* 1936 p. 42, 1937 p. 27, 1938 p. 39. In the 1960s 180 or 190 seems to have been the usual number of entrants (MO24/11/12; *League News* 1970 p.11, 1971 p. 10), but in 1966 there were 253 (*League News* 1967 p. 31).
63. *League News* 1966 p. 24; MO24/11/5; MO24/32/3–4.
64. MO23/2 p. 53; *League News* 1970 p. 17. The Sisters' study days introduced in 1951 had been discontinued because of pressure of pre-registration teaching (MO24/11/14), but study days were reintroduced for Sisters and staff nurses in 1969 (MO23/2 p. 43).
65. *League News* 1967 p. 32; MO24/32/4.

CHAPTER 6

1. L. Granshaw, *St Mark's Hospital, London: a social history of a specialist hospital* (London, 1985), p. 408.
2. The term 'School of Nursing' had often been used at St Bartholomew's in earlier years but was not recognised as a formal title until 1974. In the 1950s and 1960s some staff thought it too pretentious (information supplied by Winifred Hector).
3. *League News* 1981 p. 15.
4. *League News* 1976 pp. 18–19.
5. MO24/32/7; *League News* 1976 pp. 19–20, 1978 pp. 8, 22.
6. MO23/2 p. 55; MO24/32/5; MO24/32/9; further information supplied by Carol Bavin.
7. MO23/2 pp. 76–7; MO24/23/3.
8. *League News* 1976 p. 19.
9. MO23/2 pp. 105–6; *League News* 1970 p. 17; *Report of the Committee on Nursing* (1972), p. 121.
10. Information supplied by Winifred Hector and Carol Bavin.
11. *Report of the Committee on Nursing* (1972), p. 143.
12. *League News* 1990 p. 27; further information supplied by Carol Bavin.
13. *League News* 1975 p. 18.
14. At the time of writing the only exceptions were Strauss, a psychiatric ward where no uniform was worn, and the children's wards where students wore uniform but Sisters did not.
15. Sylvia Docking had been trained in Bournemouth but Pamela Hibbs was Bart's-trained and a former gold medallist. She was Sister Bowlby 1969–71, Senior Nursing Officer 1972–6 and Hackney Divisional Nursing Officer 1976–82: *League News* 1979 p. 17, 1983 p. 11.

16. *League News* 1981 pp. 22–3; Granshaw, *St Mark's Hospital*, pp. 410–11.

17. *League News* 1987 p. 16.

18. *St Bartholomew's School of Nursing Annual Report* 1987/8; *League News* 1990 pp. 28–9.

19. Information supplied by Carol Bavin.

20. *League News* 1990 p. 26.

21. *St Bartholomew's School of Nursing Annual Report* 1987/8. In 1971 there were 543 students (MO24/32/3).

22. *League News* 1975 p. 10, 1990 pp. 28, 32.

23. *League News* 1990 pp. 29–30.

24. *St Bartholomew's School of Nursing Annual Report* 1987/8.

25. *League News* 1990 pp. 32–3; *St Bartholomew's College of Nursing and Midwifery Annual Report* 1991; further information supplied by Susan Studdy.

26. *League News* 1987 p. 24.

27. 35 graduate teachers and 34 non-graduates were listed in the *St Bartholomew's College of Nursing and Midwifery Annual Report* 1992.

28. *League News* 1990 pp. 32, 34–5; further information supplied by Margaret Cartwright.

29. *League News* 1975 p. 15, 1976 p. 15, 1978 p.8; Granshaw, *St Mark's Hospital*, p. 409; *St Bartholomew's School of Nursing Annual Report* 1987/8.

30. *League News* 1990 p. 26; *St Bartholomew's College of Nursing and Midwifery Annual Report* 1991, 1992.

31. *City and Hackney Health District Nursing Research Papers* no. 1 (1983); M. Versluysen, 'Pathenogenesis of Pressure Sores in Elderly Patients' (typescript, *c.*1986/7).

32. *City and Hackney Health District Nursing Research Papers* no. 2 (1983); *League News* 1984 pp. 22–4.

33. *St Bartholomew's College of Nursing and Midwifery Annual Report* 1993; further information supplied by Susan Studdy and Margaret Cartwright.

34. *City and Hackney Health Authority: Annual Report of the Quality of Care Unit* 1986–90.

35. *League News* 1991 p. 6, 1992 p. 7; A. Hopkins (ed.), *The Role of Hospital Consultants in Clinical Directorates* (London, 1993), p. 13.

36. *City and Hackney Provider Unit Nursing Newsletter* April 1991; Hopkins (ed.), *Clinical Directorates*, pp. 17–20.

37. Information supplied by Pamela Hibbs.

38. *League News* 1989 pp. 5–6, 1992 p. 7; further information supplied by Pamela Hibbs.

39. Cf. Granshaw, *St Mark's Hospital*, pp. 306–7.

40. *An Application for Trust Status: the St Bartholomew's, Royal London and London Chest Hospitals NHS Trust* (London, 1993), pp. 15–16; Hopkins (ed.), *Clinical Directorates*, p. 17.

41. *An Application for Trust Status*, pp. 64–5; *The Times* 30 July 1994.

42. *League News* 1994 p. 7.

43. *League News* 1990 p. 31; *St Bartholomew's College of Nursing and Midwifery Annual Report* 1991, 1992; further information supplied by Susan Studdy.

44. *St Bartholomew's College of Nursing and Midwifery Annual Report* 1991, 1993; J. Smith (ed.), *London After Tomlinson* (London, 1993), pp. 82–3; further information supplied by Margaret Cartwright.

45. *St Bartholomew's College of Nursing and Midwifery Annual Report* 1993.

46. *St Bartholomew's College of Nursing and Midwifery Annual Report* 1993; *College Newsletter* December 1992; further information supplied by Susan Studdy and Margaret Cartwright.

ILLUSTRATIONS

The illustrations in this book are taken from the following sources at St Bartholomew's Hospital:

Chapter 4
p. 56: Archives, X8/548
p. 57: Archives, X8/717
p. 60: Dept. of Medical Photography, no. 80477
p. 61: Archives, X8/337
p. 63 (top): Archives, X8/294
p. 63 (bottom): Archives, X8/256
p. 66: Archives, X8/223
p. 67: Archives, X8/473
p. 71: Archives, X8/852
p. 73: Archives, X8/579
p. 75: Archives, X8/809
p. 77: Archives, X8/705
p. 78: Archives, X8/415

Chapter 5
p. 81: Archives, X8/621
p. 84: Archives, X68/3
p. 85: Dept. of Medical Photography, no. 9153
p. 86: Dept. of Medical Photography, no. 10116
p. 87: College of Nursing and Midwifery
p. 88: Archives, X8/755
p. 91: Archives, X8/766
p. 93: Dept. of Medical Photography, no. 59311
p. 95: Archives, X8/567
p. 98: Archives, X8/961
p. 102: Dept. of Medical Photography, no. 69659
p. 103: Dept. of Medical Photography, no. 70191
p. 105: Dept. of Medical Photography, no. 80302A

Chapter 6
p. 109: Dept. of Medical Photography, no. 99429
p. 110: Dept. of Medical Photography, no. 99428
p. 111: *League News* 1983 p. 88
p. 112: Dept. of Medical Photography, no. 103406
pp. 115, 117, 119, 124, 128: College of Nursing and Midwifery
p. 129: Dept. of Medical Photography, no. 2.92 V57/10

MATRONS OF ST BARTHOLOMEW'S HOSPITAL, AND THEIR SUCCESSORS

1547–1558/9	Rose Fisher	1781–1803	Ann Ernst
1558/9–1584	Ellen Smyth	1803–1816	Mary Foote
1584–1593	Elizabeth Jennings	1816–1819	Elizabeth
1593–1597	Mary Williamson[1]		Tompkins
1597–1623	Elizabeth Collston	1819–1836	Mary Williams
1623	Judith Taylor	1837–1845	Henrietta Baker
1623–1639/40	Jane Andrews	1845–1865	Charlotte Baker
1639/40–1643	Mary Lyatt	1865–1878	Frances Drake
1643–1674/5	Margaret Blague	1878–1881	Maria Machin
1674/5–1697	Mary Libanus	1881–1887	Ethel Manson[2]
1697–1714	Mary Sanders	1887–1910	Isla Stewart
1714–1727/8	Elizabeth Barber	1910–1927	Annie McIntosh
1727/8–1728	Elizabeth Paris	1927–1949	Helen Dey
1728–1753	Ann Hyde	1949–1967	Joan Loveridge
1753–1767	Elizabeth	1968–1974	Rhona Jones[3]
	Browning	1974–1975	Gwendoline
1767–1775	Susannah		Gardiner[4]
	Robinson	1975–1982	Mary Armstrong[4]
1775–1781	Martha Sandiford	1982–	Pamela Hibbs[5]

1. Married 1594, became Mary Price
2. Later Mrs Bedford Fenwick
3. From 1969 Chief Nursing Officer
4. District Nursing Officer, City and Hackney District
5. District Nursing Officer; from 1990 Chief Nurse and Director of Quality Assurance

Senior staff at the School of Nursing

1925–1942   Margaret Hitch[1]
1942–1946   Gwendolen Fellows[2]
1946–1970   Winifred Hector[3]
1970–1981   Helen Collyer[4]
1981–1987   Sylvia Docking[5]
1987–   Susan Studdy[6]

1. Sister Tutor; from 1929 Senior Sister Tutor
2. Senior Sister Tutor
3. Principal Tutor
4. Principal Nursing Officer (teaching division); from 1974 Director of Nurse Education
5. Director of Nurse Education
6. Director of Nurse Education; from 1989 Principal of the College of Nursing and Midwifery

INDEX

Entries in bold type refer to illustrations.

Community nursing, 109–10, 121, 122
Computers, **124**
Cookery, training in, 46, 60
Council for National Academic Awards, 120
Covent Garden, 80
Cox Davies, Rachael, 54, 56, 58
Cross, William Henry, 28, 30
Cupping, 64

Darenth (Kent), 42
Davies, Mary, 46–7
Deputy Matron, 99
Dermatology, 76, 83
Dey, Helen, 70–2, **71**, 74, 76, 79, 82, 103
Dickens, Charles, 18
Dietetics, 76, 83
Diphtheria, 72
Director of Nurse Education, 108, 115, 118
Directors of Nursing Services, 124
District Management Team, 107, 114
District Nursing Officer, 107–8, 116, 122, 123, 125
Divisional Nursing Officers, 107–8, 124
Docking, Sylvia, 115
Dominion nurses, 100
Drake, Frances, 28, 31, 34
Dressers, 33
Dressings, 16, 33, 61, 62, **63**, 74, 92, 104
Drugs and medicines, 9–10, 17, 27, 46, 64
Dubarcow, Ann, 19
Duckworth, Dyce, 32–3, 46
Dynn, Lettice, 11

Ear, nose and throat, diseases of, 76, 83
Eastern Hospital, 42, 107, 108
Economics, study of, 96
Edeva, 2–3
Edinburgh University, 96
Emetics, 16

Enemas, 16, 46
English National Board for Nursing and Midwifery, 120, 122
Enrolled nurses, 103–4, 115, 121
Ethics, study of, 64, 117, 123
Evans, Mary Ann, 21

Family planning, 122
Federated Superannuation Scheme, 72
Fellows, Gwendolen, 79
Fenwick, Mrs Bedford: *see* Manson, Ethel Gordon
Fevers, 25, 64
Films, 84, 104, **105**
Finsbury, 40, **60**
First World War, 58
Fisher, Rose, 5
Flack, Nurse, 22
Fomentations, 16, 61
Foote, Mary, 15
Foundling Hospital, 31
France, 53

Gamp, Sarah, 18
Gardiner, Gwendoline, 107
General Nursing Council, 58–9, 70, 80, 85, 94, 104, 105, 111, 116, 120
Geriatric nursing, 110
German Hospital, 107, 108
Gibbs, James, 12
Gloucester, Duchess of, 109
Gloucester, Duke of, 90
Governors, Board of, 5, 7–15, **14**, 17, 20, **21**, 24, 28–30, 32–4, 38, 41, 54, 55, 60, 80–2, 85, 97, 107
Guy's Hospital, 59, 124
Gynaecological nursing, 46, 64, 83

Hackney, 42, 105, 107–12, 116
Hackney Hospital, 107, 108, 126
Hackney School of Nursing, 108–10, 111, 112
Hall, Elsie, 70
Harvey, William, 9

Patients:
  admission and discharge, 5, 15, 22, 114
  air-raid casualties, 77–8
  allocation to wards, 5, 7, 15, 114–15
  church attendance, 18
  clothing, 15
  conduct, 8, 9, 11, 17
  convalescence, 33, 114
  deaths, 16, 17
  dependency levels, 114, 122
  food and drink, 2, 5, 7, 16, 17, 24, 43, 45, 62, 64, 88
  helping Sisters and nurses, 8, 15, 38
  illustrations, **13**, **41**, **66**
  numbers, 5, 24
  nursing care, 2, 7, 16–17, 22, 33, 52, 116, 122–3
  sailors, 8, 11
  soldiers, 8, **9**, 11, 58, 77
  wartime evacuation, 76, **77**
  washing, 5, 7, 8, 15, 33, 43, 46, 62, 104
'Patients' Charter', 123
Pendlebury (Lancs.), Children's Hospital, 47
Pensions, 11, 35, 72
Pertenhale, Joan de, 3–4
Pertenhale, William de, 3
Philadelphia, 47
Physicians, 9, 45, 46, 48, 58, 62
Physiology, 32, 46, 60, 64, 105, 117
Piggott's Manor, 83, **84**, 105
Plague, 10
Platt Report, 94
Pool of Bethesda, The, **13**
Preliminary Training School, 59–61, **60**, 76, 83–4, **84**, 86, **102**, 105–6
President, 5, 20, 89
Pressure sores, 122–3
Prig, Betsey, 18
Princess Alexandra and Newham College of Nursing and Midwifery, 130

Principal, College of Nursing and Midwifery, 118, 127, 130
Principal Nursing Officers, 99
Principal Tutor, 79, 85, 86, **95**, 99
Probationers, 30–3, **34**, 36, 38–42, **44**, 46, 49–50, 57–8, 59–65, 68–9, 70, 74, 82
Probationers on trial, 38, 42
Project 2000, 120–2, 127
Prontosil, 74
Psychiatric nursing, 86, 96, 105, 110, 111
Psychology, 83, 96, 117, 127
Public health, 64
Pupil nurses, 104, 105, 108, 110, 112, **112**, 121

Quality assurance, 123, 125

Rahere, 1
Rawlins, Jane, 11
Registration, campaign for, 42, 53–4, 55–6, 58
Religion, 1, 5, 7, 17–18, 35, 70–2
Renal nursing, 122
Research, 122–3
Resource Allocation Working Party, 125
Robinson, Susannah, 13, **14**
Royal College of Nursing, 55–6, 72, 94, 123
Royal Free Hospital, 54
Royal Hospitals NHS Trust, 126
Royal London Hospital: *see* London Hospital
Rushcliffe Committee, 80

St Albans (Herts.), 76
St Bartholomew and Princess Alexandra and Newham College of Nursing and Midwifery, 130; *see also* Nurses, training and education
St Bartholomew the Great, church of, 1
St Bartholomew the Less, church of, 17, 20, 72